The educational **poetry** competition combining literacy and history

Travel Back in Rhyme

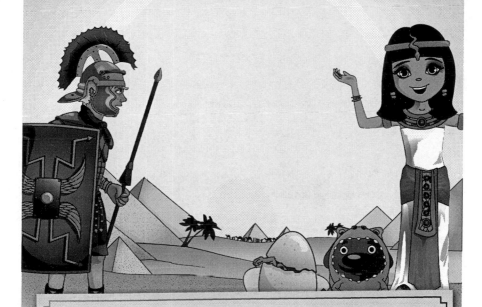

Scotland & Northern England

First published in Great Britain in 2012 by:

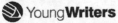 Young**Writers**

Remus House
Coltsfoot Drive
Peterborough
PE2 9BF
Telephone: 01733 890066
Website: www.youngwriters.co.uk

Foreword

Young Writers was established in 1991, dedicated to encouraging reading and creative writing by young people. Our nationwide writing initiatives are designed to inspire ideas and the incentive to write, and in turn develop literacy skills and confidence, whilst participating in a fun, imaginative activity. The final reward is the opportunity for the budding young writer to see their work in print.

Our latest competition, Travel Back In Rhyme, focuses on using historical periods, events or people to inspire poetry. The resulting collection is an illuminating glimpse into the past through the eyes of our young generation. There is verse inspired by everything from dinosaurs and cavemen, to the ancient civilisations of Greece and Egypt, to the World Wars and even space travel. The talented young poets have created verse that is gory, funny, dramatic, tragic: a reflection of human history up to the present day.

Using a mix of imagination, expression and historical inspiration, this anthology is an impressive snapshot of the inventive, original and skilful writing of young people today. With the extra bonus of fun fact pages about some of history's best bits, this collection is a journey back in time that will delight readers for years to come.

Contents

The Poetry

World War II

What can I see?
I can see Berlin on the edge of war,
Executions taking place,
Burly soldiers – tears down their faces,
And to put it simply –
Torture.

Innocent children getting shot in a second,
Machine gunners becking.
I can see misery.
People staring at me,
Like I'm a God.

What can I feel?
Power.
Constantly growing fear,
Constantly shrinking misery.
Above all,
A slight twinge of madness in me,
Death,
Responsibility – growing stage by stage,
Temper – something I use very often to get what I want,
Tears – a lot (they maybe top my misery).

What can I hear?
Noise.
Bombs going boom!
Never-ending screams,
Blasts from tanks,
Yells,
Hanamangs exploding,
Helmets clattering,
Whispers – about me.
I'm going mad.
To hear peace would be a dream come true.
Birds chirping happily – not in agony,
But hearing peace is hearing defeat.

Finlay MacVicar (10)
Balivanich Primary School, Benbecula

World War II

What can I see?
Bodies in fields.
My soldier's fight.
Bombings.
Guns on the ground.
Blood on walls.
Nazi helmets.
Explosions.

What can I feel?
Dirt on my face.
My moustache.
Mud on my camouflage.
My Nazi badge.
My gun.
My magazine.

What can I hear?
Gun fire.
Bombs dropping,
Jets flying over my head.
Helicopters hovering over my head.
Explosions.
Harriers.

Lewis MacDonald (9)
Balivanich Primary School, Benbecula

Untitled

I can see the rain drops from the rainforest,
The little fishes jumping about.

I can feel my light colourful wings,
The wet water,
And my hard beak.

I can hear the splashes from ponds,
Quacking from ducks,
And the noise from streets close to me.

Andrew Muncaster (8)
Balivanich Primary School, Benbecula

World War II

What can I see?
Graves and guns,
Blood splashed everywhere,
Enemies coming closer,
The tents full of people –
With fear and tears.
Half the British population dead.

What can I feel?
My heart about to come out my throat,
My eye about to come out.
I'm about to drop dead.
Blood coming out my nose.
My camouflage about to come off.

What can I hear?
Nazis shouting to get cover,
Soldiers heading back to Berlin,
Planes ready for take-off,
Tanks blowing up.

Calum Craib (11)
Balivanich Primary School, Benbecula

I Am Boudicca

The swords being sharpened by my warriors
The Romans trudging towards us
The blood running from my warriors

Our battle cry roaring above the crowd
They killed my husband but
I say
'I am Boudicca and we will fight.'

Romans retreating, victory is ours
The long grass stroking against my feet
While I run
But
The Romans catch me.

Iona MacKay (11)
Balivanich Primary School, Benbecula

3

What Can I See?

What can I see?
Slaves,
Weapons,
Pharaohs,
Mummies,
The dark sarcophagus,
All my gold.

What can I feel?
The wet bandages,
The cold coffin,
Loneliness.

What can I hear?
The sound of my slaves complaining,
The sound of gold falling out of my pots,
My animals.

Megan Mackay (8)
Balivanich Primary School, Benbecula

What Can I See?

What can I see?
Lots of other underwater animals,
Lots of people diving,
Lots of nice food for me (hooray!)
Some of my friends,
Some of my favourite toys,
People getting stung by me.

What can I feel?
Lots of wet water,
Some of my friends bumping into me.

What can I hear?
Lots of people shouting at me (oh no!)
The ocean waters waving against me,
My family calling me (come home now).

Kyra Stephenson (8)
Balivanich Primary School, Benbecula

4

Viking

What can I see?
Weapons lying all around,
People dying,
Blood pouring out of my wounds,
People are frightened.

What can I feel?
Fear shaking through my bones,
Anger all around me.
Violence running down my veins,
Blood running down my head.

What can I hear?
People shouting from their longboats,
Waves crashing.

Elisa Morrison (8)
Balivanich Primary School, Benbecula

Soldier

What can I see?
Bodies in the fields,
Tanks, weapons, broken trees, enemies, soldiers,
People jumping out of helicopters, aircraft closing in.

What can I feel?
My helmet, my boots, my clothes, the wind.
My heart is beating faster.

What can I hear?
The wind, bombs exploding,
Helicopters flying over my head,
Tanks moving slowly,
Helicopters dropping bombs.
I can hear tanks blowing up.

Kian Humberstone (7)
Balivanich Primary School, Benbecula

Untitled

What can I see?
Under the water,
Up in the sky,
Lots of trees down below.

What can I feel?
The water pushing me up and down,
The wind pushing me away,
The branches falling down.
My feathers tickling me.

What can I hear?
My singing,
The sea roaring,
The wind blowing.

Chloe Humberstone (8)
Balivanich Primary School, Benbecula

What Can I See?

What can I see?
I can see bodies lying all around me,
Patches of blood on the battlefields,
People fighting their hearts out for their country.

What can I feel?
I can feel the pain of others,
The ground shake as a bomb goes off in the distance.
I can feel the pain of the loved ones left behind.

What can I hear?
I can hear the sound of swords clashing,
The sound of guns firing.

Laura MacKay (11)
Balivanich Primary School, Benbecula

Who Am I?

I see a house on fire,
Little children screaming for someone to rescue them
And the people that work with me getting ready to spray
The water on the fire.

A firebell ringing because there is a fire
An ambulance coming where the fire is in case people might be hurt
And the fire cracking and popping.

I can feel the sweat dripping down my head because of the fire
The smoke from the fire is hurting my eyes and little drops of water from the
hose hitting my arm.

Rhiannon Bagley (8)
Balivanich Primary School, Benbecula

World War II

I can see my comrades fading,
Deep inside the poppy field,
Under the dreaded black sky.

I can feel my heart failing,
As death is opening in this war.
But the pride for my nation keeps me fighting.

I can hear my body slipping,
And the screaming of a gun,
Showing no mercy:
'Man down! Man down!'

Kirsty Macdonald (10)
Balivanich Primary School, Benbecula

Untitled

I can see dolphins jumping out of the water repeatedly
Out at the open sea,
My fellow family members,
Hunting for fish with me.

I can feel the salty presence of the sea,
Fish struggling to get out of my giant mouth,
Water spewing out of my blow hole.

I can hear the waves crashing against others,
My fellow family members,
Calling for me.

Kenny Ballantyne (8)
Balivanich Primary School, Benbecula

Who Am I?

I can see a little mouse scuttling along the green grass.
I can see fish in a large fish tank.
I can see my owner putting food in my bowl.
I can taste yummy milk from my bowl.
I can taste a mouse in my mouth trying to survive.
I can taste my fur from my body.
I can smell my litter box.
I can smell dogs hiding to get me.
I can smell flowers growing in the garden.
I can feel my owners stroking me and washing me.

Rinchen Coleman (7)
Balivanich Primary School, Benbecula

Cleopatra

Egyptian walls
My maids weaving brand new silk dress as
I sink into my milk bath.

People talking
Wild animals

Gentle covers on my bed.
Everything around me.

Emma Macdonald (10)
Balivanich Primary School, Benbecula

Roman War

Slaves stabbed and skinned alive
With blood everywhere.

The screams of babies and men fighting for their lives.
Dead everywhere.

The screams of souls in my heart.
The sadness of people being shot in the head with a bow and arrow.

Duncan Rossi (11)
Balivanich Primary School, Benbecula

A Dinosaur World

Trees.
Logs.
Other dinosaurs.
Hunters.
Wood.
Spiky and soft flowers.

Neil Martin Macdonald (9)
Balivanich Primary School, Benbecula

A Dinosaur's World

Tree
Hill
Tyrant lizards
Sound
Mad
Angry.

Reanne Ireland (10)
Balivanich Primary School, Benbecula

World Wars

What can I hear?
I can hear the loud guns firing back and forth
Throughout the dark windy night.
I can also hear huge bombs exploding on the grounds
Of this old but great earth,
And terrified soldiers shouting loud orders across
The deserted battlefield.
I can hear buildings tumbling down everywhere.
Sirens are going off everywhere deafening my ears.

What can I see?
I can see our great Earth in danger.
I can also see barrage balloons floating in the dark sky,
To keep the loud German planes away.
On the deserted battlefield I see a tough gang of big soldiers shooting bullets
from their long silver rifle guns,
Into innocent people's bodies.
I can also see a huge bomb exploding in front of my very own eyes.
It has red and orange sparks as bright as the sun
And thick black smoke.

What do I feel?
I feel the hard ground shaking below my small pale feet.
I also feel a slight drop of a clear tear dripping down
From my golden eyes.
I feel a lot of emotions just now but the one terrible thing is
That I feel so devastated.

Anna Ferguson (11)
Birkhill Primary School, Birkhill

World War II

I can see . . .
Shells flying through the air,
Giant deadly tanks everywhere,
Army troops all around,
Giant trenches in the ground,
Winston Churchill, British Prime Minister,
And Germany's Hitler who is sinister,
People screaming like they're mad,
Vile traitors, now they *are* bad,
That's what I can see.
I can hear . . .
People screaming off their heads,
People mourning over the dead,
Guns shooting day and night,
Hoping they could end this fight,
Fighter planes in the sky,
People eating rationed pie,
The scratching of pens writing home,
Telling their family they're not alone,
As lots and lots of other guys,
Fight and sometimes lose their lives,
That's what I can hear,
I can feel . . .
Sadness in the air,
Cos the enemy don't care,
The trigger of a gun,
That every day kills someone,
The lice that can invade your body,
These wars are very bloody,
That's what I can feel
Now this lousy war has ended,
There are things that can't be mended,
The pain that people have gone through,
It could've killed me and you,
There's something that can't be forgot,
The people in the war that fought!

James Taylor (10)
Birkhill Primary School, Birkhill

The Vikings

Great warriors, sword and shield,
Blood running through the fields,
This was in the time of the Vikings!
Spears flying through the air
Fires burning like a flare
All terrible deeds of the Vikings.
Curses yelled all through the night,
Everyone looking for a fight,
Some violent hobbies of the Vikings.
Longboats charged ahead
Vikings fought till they were dead.
You may not like it but they were Vikings!
Swords clashed like thunder and lightning,
They were all addicted to fighting,
They acted like gorillas but they were Vikings!
Bloody screams in the fight
Dead bodies in the night.
People full of violence, the Vikings.
Out of the mist axes appeared
Everyone was hiding in fear
The violent attack of the Vikings!
Blood everywhere
Loads of people stabbed and lame
Just like a very, very violent video game.
These were the violent murderous strikes of the Vikings!
Here is a strange surprise
The Vikings were actually nice!
But only at home
They were the Vikings!

Ciarán Haut (11)
Birkhill Primary School, Birkhill

Mary's Execution

Mary's head on the guillotine
With the bloody axe at her feet.
Hearing gunshots and dogs barking
The king shouting orders, oh how sad it would be.
I hear the axes and the guillotine
Oh I wish I was at home.
I hear the horses galloping like thunder
Oh I wonder.
I see the blood, I see the tears
I am trembling in fear.
I see the red blood on the sharp shiny axe
I see the guillotine with blood as red as strawberries
I also see Mary's dog
Barking on her knee
While the piles of blood are
Rushing down the road
I feel guilt, I feel sad
I feel powerful, I feel glad
I feel blood, I feel sorrow
I feel bad, I feel the blame
I feel the cold wind in her hair
I feel scared
I feel disappointed
I feel ashamed
. . . I am her cousin
I am Elizabeth, the lady who
Made this happen!

Sophie Warden (11)
Birkhill Primary School, Birkhill

Mary Queen Of Scots

The last thing Mary saw was a great brick wall
And the first thing the crowd saw was her head fall.
Mary's dog was shaking like an earthquake, the dog was depressed.
When Mary's head dropped into the brown glossy wicker basket
You heard a gigantic thump.
The gory guillotine was now covered in scarlet blood which dripped every time
you looked at it.
I could feel depression in the air everywhere.
The executor was dressed like darkness.

The king's men were here again, raising the English flag
It was waving like the sea.
A teenager screaming from the back of the crowd
His mum was dead, he had grief all over his face.
The crowd was gloomy like it was before but now
With a little bit more.
Peasants were standing there like stone
I could hear her heart pounding.

Elizabeth regretful for what she had done, killed her cousin Mary.
Mary's dog as furry as a bear as everyone cared.
Death in the air, I could feel it coming towards me
As her son cried as he lay on the ground.
I wanted to help him but I knew I would cause commotion
So I left him.
I felt bad as he was being dragged away
But that's the price I had to pay.
I could see a tear in Elizabeth's eye, I knew she would cry.

Rachel Alexander (11)
Birkhill Primary School, Birkhill

Vikings

I see them coming
They look ferocious
I see the longboat, just as vicious.
The oars are made from
A dull grey wood like an old dirty boot.

I see small straw-made huts
I hear the longboat
On the shore
Swords clanging and so much more.

I hear people screaming
Like wild animals.
I hear a longboat.
The waves are
Smashing like a storm has hit.
I feel scared and worried.
I hide behind
A rusted old wooden barrel.

Once more I hear a scream.
I see one of the invaders
He is looking at me.
I pray and pray he is not going to come for me.
He steps over
He says to me, 'Little boy, come with me.'

Jack Smith (10)
Birkhill Primary School, Birkhill

All The Soldiers Are Dead

All the soldiers are dead
All the soldiers are dead
Running from red pools of blood
All we can hear is bangs
And guns firing and men screaming
'Help me, help me!'
All the soldiers are dead
All the soldiers are dead.

Nicholas Findlay (9)
Birkhill Primary School, Birkhill

The Vikings!

We loaded up the boat with food and swords
For our long trip ahead.
The sea was as wild as a horse
We rode as strong as an ox,
We sailed for days,
Not stopping once for a break or rest
But we made it after a long trip of many days
We finally got to the destination of our trip
Scotland!
As you heard, the babies were crying
As the battle went on people started dropping like flies.
You heard cries of people in pain
You could hear the swords clanging
Up and down the island
After it was over they started to take everything.
It wasn't long till they went back to the boat
Again they had to sail for days on end
But they had victory.
When they got home
They held an enormous celebration
There was roast chicken and gravy
As they planned
What they would do with
All the stolen goods!

Davey Begg (10)
Birkhill Primary School, Birkhill

The Battle

Stomp! Stomp! A big army comes charging through the forest
Ting! Ting! The sound of soldiers fighting for life.

Here comes William Wallace
With his big long sword
Bashing, slashing everyone in the night sky.

Men dying all around
The gory cry of soldiers is the only sound.

Luke Scott (9)
Birkhill Primary School, Birkhill

World War II

When I heard
The siren I
Was as scared
As a timid mouse
I saw a plane crash
Into a house.
I heard the fire roar
Like a lion as I watched
People dying.
I heard the guns
They were as loud as thunder.
Then I looked under I saw . . .
A valuable thing.
It was a golden ring.
I saw children screaming
And their mothers weeping.
I walked home to see
That my house was just rubble
I fell on my hands and knees.
I was as upset as Santa Claus
With no Christmas
I was so lonely, I had no one
There were people running, crying
. . . Even children dying.

Lucie Soutar (11)
Birkhill Primary School, Birkhill

Wait And Wonder

I'm waiting for my dad, I hope he comes back
I'm waiting for my dad, I hope he's not under attack
I'm wanting him to come to Mum and I
And I'm hoping he will not die
My dad came in through the door
I won, I won, no fighting any more.

Zoe Neilson (9)
Birkhill Primary School, Birkhill

Mary Queen Of Scots

Sad faces here and there, how could we stop this tragic fear?
People screaming so loud the whole town could hear them
So much violence from such a small town
Kings and queens rule the town
People die trying to steal their crown.
People beheaded for no such reason
I hate them all
We should be killing them not the other way round.
Mary Queen of Scots was beheaded, there was no reason
For executing.
They are such bad people, I wish they'd die
With all the worst people
They killed innocent children
So selfish
We should have them killed but they are too strong
I lost the plot in 1865 when they killed Mary Queen of Scots
I tried to kill them but I could not do it.
I hope one day someone will kill one of them.
Young children pray every day that they would die
They should die for the trouble they caused.
Not one person would care for them.
They once died but the people who replaced them
Were just as bad.

Ross Jamieson (11)
Birkhill Primary School, Birkhill

Wallace And Bruce

Metal banging on other metal.
Metal banging on other metal.
Gloopy blood like ketchup on a plate.
You hear the cries of dying soldiers.
The fire as bright as the sun.
All that's left are bones of soldiers.
Families pray for their sons to be OK.
Metal banging on other metal.
Metal banging on other metal.

Hannah Burns (9)
Birkhill Primary School, Birkhill

Vikings

I see a ship along the big blue sea going as fast as the eyes can see.
Coming faster and faster, I wonder who it is . . .
Oh no, it is the Vikings
Everyone run.
Running, running as fast as I can
I tripped, oh no
They're at the other side
Quickly go back and hide.
I see my friends get chased.
Then I see my dad fighting with his sword, this way, that way.
'Watch out,' I say but it is too late
He is gone, murdered in front of my eyes.
My home is on fire.
'Rahhhh!' says one Viking, 'you're coming with me.'
Suddenly I am in Denmark being a slave
Picking up rubbish and told to behave
Treated like dirt and sleeping in hay.
Walking around, trying to be normal and find a place.
When I'm around I try to forgive them for what they did
I'll never be normal, I'll never behave
I'll always be Scottish and I know I will.
I'll never forgive them for treating me that way
And always remember what they did that day.

David Simpson (11)
Birkhill Primary School, Birkhill

Egyptians

The jingling of the jewellery is in my ear,
Hearing the pharaoh isn't clear,
Eating now loudly so I don't hear,
Every child playing in the sand,
Great to see the waving hands,
You are getting burnt by the sun but it doesn't spoil the fun,
The large beautiful pyramids are very well done,
And the beige bandages on the mummies are nicely done,
Now the wind is blowing while the people are growing fruit in the blazing sun.

Louise Anderson (11)
Birkhill Primary School, Birkhill

19

King Edward

God help me
I'm going to fight for Edward
I'm so afraid
My lungs are falling off
My knees are shaking
Oh no, here's my dad
Ready to trade
Me for his life
And I'm only young
Sixteen years to be exact
I've got all my stuff, two loaves of bread and a jug of water
Halfway to Stirling I am
But now my dad's dead
With his violet red blood
Dirty like an evil red heart
It's a foggy way
I can see the battle
Lots of men lost their lives
That old man took my dad
I'm going to kill that bad old man
Here I go into battle
I almost lost my life
I feel proud to be a Scottish man.

Mikee Harry Connelly (9)
Birkhill Primary School, Birkhill

Ancient Egypt

The River Nile is rushing fast
While I watch it go past
The pyramids have points like swords
And the sand is as yellow as mustard

All I can hear is water from the Nile
And pharaohs giving commands
People also clapping their hands
And waving some fans

I stood under the massive pyramids
Staring amazed
As I gazed
All so amazed

Sphinx everywhere
Like I cared
As they stared
All around at me

I kept on walking
Through the gentle, soft sand
With my feet feeling grand
As they went through the sand.

Rachel King (11)
Birkhill Primary School, Birkhill

It's All Gone

Everything had gone
Everything had gone
All that foggy smoke covering the area.
The blood dripping from the dead was as red as strawberries.
The place was like a graveyard full of dead people.
The dirty dead bones were as dirty as mud.
I could see the land was as red as tomato soup.
The lives of people were shattered
Everything had gone
Everything had gone.

Soha Nabi (9)
Birkhill Primary School, Birkhill

9/11

Ring! Firemen to the rescue,
Ring! Firemen to the rescue,
In the truck we went to save them,
Up and down the streets we went,
To help all the people.

People were terrified, running down the building hall,
Crash! Smash! Humans would rather fall,
Up and up the steps we did,
Some humans hid.

The 1st plane hit,
Everyone was frightened,
Trying to save all we can,
We helped them, then ran,

The 2nd plane crashed
The building fell like dust,
We couldn't see a single thing,
We tried, but thousands died,
Ring! Firemen to the rescue,
Ring! Firemen to the rescue.

Eilidh Robertson (10)
Birkhill Primary School, Birkhill

Time Travel

The world started with the Big Bang
Diplodocus had a long neck
Egyptians made pyramids, they were high-tech
Pharaohs became mummies
Romans watched the Coliseum dummies
Gladiators got chased by lions
Pirates drank a lot of rum
Victorians lasted the time of Queen Vic
World War II started with Hitler, the lunatic
Now we're back in our time and place
But I wonder if the world will survive
for the rest of the human race.

Fraser Dingwall (9)
Birkhill Primary School, Birkhill

Queen Mary

Mary Queen of Scots
I can hear the gunshots
I am covered in blood blots
I can hear the rusty dungeon doors slamming
Massive horses galloping
Sadness in the air as we say our prayers
I can see the castle
I can see the guillotine
I can see the heartbreak of the queen
I can see the dog sitting on her knee
I can see the flowers in the garden
I can see the soldiers getting ready to shoot
I can't look as they shoot innocent people
In my dungeon all alone I sit and wonder who is gone?
Then I feel the horses gallop past like thunder
A cold wind runs past me, what could that be?
The sun blazes past me.
Who could that be in front of me?
Sadness and sorrow lash me
I wonder what will happen to me?

Katharine Leonard (11)
Birkhill Primary School, Birkhill

The War Of William Wallace

Scarlet blood on the street
A red-blooded sun
The wolves have something to eat
Swords are slashing together somewhere gory
The dirty dead fling into my lonely street
The dread of the sons getting ready for war
Getting stabbed in the stomach
Loads of gore
Hands in the air
Shields on the arm
Going back in time is never a bore.

Jonah Toth (9)
Birkhill Primary School, Birkhill

23

Mary Queen Of Scots

What I see.
I see a big black castle and a crown the size of the sea.
I see long windows and long pitch-black hallways
And thrones the size of me
I see an axe as shiny as a mirror.

What I hear.
I hear a dog howling, guns shooting and screaming
I hear the king giving commands
And footsteps in the hallways and squeaking in the floorboards.
I hear the wind blowing through the curtains and the wind blowing through my
pure white bed covers.

What I feel.
I feel walls and as I touch them they crumble into pieces
I feel so scared
I feel rough dresses and a heavy gold crown.
As I head my way outside the long grass up to my knees tickles me and may
give me fleas
I get the shivers as the rain lands on my head
I think to myself, *can we really make the world a better place?*

Hope Carrie (10)
Birkhill Primary School, Birkhill

World War II

I could smell the fear
The crows were having the feast of a lifetime
The fields were like a graveyard full of dead bodies
The world was like a ghost town
The lives of many were shattered
The dead people's bones were as black as a dark cave
The fields were full of plane wrecks
I searched for days
But couldn't find my family
Suddenly I saw my father among the dead
What a pitiful sight!

Kienan Agley (9)
Birkhill Primary School, Birkhill

24

Wallace And Bruce

Red blood
Foggy smoke
Smelly fields
Wallace's sword
Violent fighting
Bruce – king

What will they think of next?
Burning fire
Metal banging
Gory crying
Soldiers dying
Fields of blood
Scary English
Mouldy bread
Why am I in this?
What now?
Wallace dying
Getting stretched
English turning home.

Cameron Winter (9)
Birkhill Primary School, Birkhill

Life As A Tree

I was so happy, watching animals play
I was so happy, just sitting there every day
I watched them grow, I watched them smile
I watched them run a thousand miles
But now it's all different, there's nothing there
None of us find it very fair
Tigers die and monkeys just lie
Birds can't land on the tree tops up high
How does this happen? I am confused
But wait!
It's man-made, people just like you
But it could get better even I know
If everyone takes part in this eco-friendly show.

Faith Smith (9)
Birkhill Primary School, Birkhill

Anne Frank

A nne Frank lived in an office
N azis wanting to kill her
N ever a peep from up above
E veryone scared

F eeling afraid myself
R aiding the street Hitler was doing
' A nything to do Mum?' 'No,' she said
N ot many friends Anne Frank had
K ind, she was sweet as sugar

A ir raid shelters filled with Jews
N azis searching home to home
D oodling she was in her diary

H itler was bad
I nteresting he was but bad
T errorising the streets
L ittering them more
E veryone is as silent as mice
R otten, he was killing many people.

Anna Findlay (11)
Birkhill Primary School, Birkhill

Dinosaur's Destiny

Dinosaurs are running
Tyrannosaurs are biting like alligators
Deinonychus are chasing down prey like lions
Triceratops are fleeing like deer
Pliosaurus are swimming like dolphins
Pterosaurs are flying like birds
Edmontosaurus are chewing their grass
Spinosaurus are catching fish like crocodiles
Giganotosaurus are attacking Argentinosaurus
Then the meteorite hit.
Bang!
The dinosaurs' reign had ended
But the mammals had just begun . . .

Ben Fleming (9)
Birkhill Primary School, Birkhill

World War II

Horses galloping
Horses galloping
World War II was going to end
I would hate to be one of them
But if I was I would just run around the bend
Horses galloping
Horses galloping

Horrible screaming
Horrible screaming
Lumpy blood dripping from bayonets
I wouldn't like to be in any of the wars
You can't stop screaming when Hitler is smashing windows,
it's horrible.
Bang, bang, bang!
Horrible screaming!
Horrible screaming!

Ellie Taylor (9)
Birkhill Primary School, Birkhill

Wallace And Bruce

The fire comes out of the metal
Swords and shields burning the fields
Bodies lying by the dying of Wallace and Bruce
Fire is as red as the sun
People dying from the wars
Dirty bones from the wars
Metal hitting metal
Foggy smoke
Trading my son's life to the English
Scarlet blood dripping on streets
Sun is shining but blood over grounds
Gory cries of dying soldiers
His soul in one piece, his body's in four.

Ryan Lawson (9)
Birkhill Primary School, Birkhill

Cross Their Path

Working morning, day and night,
Victorian housemaids better sleep tight,
Of all the things they have to do,
The worst thing is cleaning the loo,
Their clothes are itchy, small and dull,
They are so skinny you can almost see their skull,
They always wish they were really rich,
And have a garden and a sports pitch,
And in the town, they'd always laugh,
When a little housemaid would cross their path.

Emily McLean (9)
Birkhill Primary School, Birkhill

World War II

All my friends were gone.
I could smell the rotten bodies in the fields.
The water was red as 1000 strawberries
I could hear the loud bangs from the planes
that were coming over our heads
All the blood dripping from the dead soldiers lying on the ground.
The crows having a feast of their life.
The dead bones of the people were as dirty as mud.
The plane crashed, there was nothing left.
The place was very much polluted.
The street was like a crater.
The lives of people were shattered.
All the smoke was as foggy as a rain cloud.
The fields were like a graveyard full of dead bodies.
Everything I knew was gone.

Jude Hughes (10)
Birkhill Primary School, Birkhill

World War II

The skies are black,
the seas are blue,
and all I'm thinking about is you.
I've been in this wretched place for days,
and I don't even have a place to stay.
I can feel the mud squelching
between my numb toes,
I just can't stop thinking about you and home.
I can see the bombs blowing up next to me,
I can hear the majors shouting
extremely loud at me.
I can't wait till this war is over,
we will be in Normandy by the time this letter is over.
The skies are black,
the seas are blue,
I just can't wait to be home with you!

Molly Hughes (11)
Birkhill Primary School, Birkhill

Victorian Education

I woke this morning very excited
Today is the day school has started.
I am nine years old and growing very fast
Mummy says the school has opened at last.

I line up straight and tall with all the girls
Apron all clean and a ribbon in my curls.
The teacher looks strict and swishes her cane
I hope I don't get whipped and feel the pain.

I sit at my desk in a straight row
Not daring to move or asking to go.
The teacher is telling us our ABC
I must learn it before I go home for tea.

I must sit very quiet and not wriggle about
Or the teacher will rap my knuckles and shout.
I must practice my writing and not blot the page
I must do it all well or I will get caned.

The discipline is harsh and makes me weep
But beats being in a chimney having to sweep.
I will do my best and I might be lucky
As I don't want to work the farmyard getting mucky.

Chloe Fairlie (9)
Calveley Primary School, Calveley

History Back In Rhyme

History in rhyme, let's start this year
Lots of flags, waves and cheer
Wills and Kate magically kissed
It was a year not to be missed
Everyone partied in the thousands
Just like the Millennium, the year 2000
Before that we partied after the wars
The Great, First, Second and Boer
Never forget to remember those that fell
And especially those who are not here to tell
In the 1800s the Victorians reigned supreme
Victoria, our longest serving queen
In the 1700s with the wigs and ruffled blouses
We had the Georgians and the big town houses
The Great Fire of London came in 1666
The city fell and couldn't be fixed
In the 1600s the Tudors reigned
Oh they caused so much pain
Henry VIII was the big Tudor king
His many wives he beheaded or something
The Romans built the roads we walk
Their taxes still taken as we talk
Mighty Vikings stopped off in York
It just seems like everyone fought
I love Robin Hood the best
Stole from the rich to give to the poorest
Middle Ages, Merlin worked his magic
If he'd been caught it would have been tragic
So here we end and put down our pen
But let's not forget those Ice Age men.

Nathan Moss (9)
Calveley Primary School, Calveley

31

Back In Time

Back, back, back in time
Back, back, back in rhyme,
To start all this off Will's enemies stood no chance,
They called him the first English King although he
came from France.

Back, back, back in time,
Back, back, back in rhyme,
400 years later Henry VIII made all women shake in fear,
Which made them come nowhere near.

Back, back, back in time,
Back, back, back in rhyme,
Huge jump to Pudding Lane,
Where everybody is praying for a lot of rain.

Back, back, back in time,
Back, back, back in rhyme,
Just after that the Industrial Revolution
Revved up Mankind's evolution.

Back, back, back in time,
Back, back, back in rhyme,
Back, back to 41,
When the sound of London was bomb, bomb, bomb.

Back, back, back in time,
Back, back, back in rhyme,
At the start of the second millennium,
I came out of my mum's tum.

James Lomas (11)
Calveley Primary School, Calveley

Stalingrad

We're on the trip to Stalingrad, we always thought Hitler was mad, I miss my family and I'm very sad, just 10 miles to go.

We're walking through the thick white snow, I never thought I'd have to go, I could die but I'll never know, just 9 more miles to go.

I'm getting very nervous now, I'm getting further away from town, My chances of survival are going down, just 8 more miles to go.

I do hope we are not lost, my nose is getting blocked with frost, Enemy lines have we crossed, just 7 more miles to go.

I'm starting to smell very rank, we have lost our left flank, I'm sad we didn't bring a tank, just 6 more miles to go.

Why can't we have a break, I'd rather be eating steak, We have coffee that'll keep me awake, just 5 more miles to go.

Now we'll have to set up camp, the only light is our oil lamp, My arm is in terrible cramp, just 4 more miles to go.

Wakey, wakey, rise and shine, I wish I had a glass of wine, This to the British is a crime, just 3 more miles to go.

We can't stop now we are too close, I want a celebratory roast, I want my feet to turn to toast, just 2 more miles to go.

We are in running distance now, my legs feel like they could crumble down, Stalingrad I am here now, just 1 more mile to go.

Now I'm here and I was there, I may as well be everywhere, It can't end this way, it isn't fair, 0 more miles to go.

Oscar Corlett-Moss (9)
Calveley Primary School, Calveley

As I Travel Back To The Warfield

As I travel back in rhyme,
I go back in time,
And find that I stand
With a gun in my hand.
Where am I?
And then I realise . . .
That I am stood staring into the midst
Of the mist.
As the battle of World War One goes on
I hear the knees of the troops rattle.
The Warfield is a stream of fright.
I bite my lip in fear.
Whilst I hear the whistle of the bombs,
The bullets flash like sparklers.
As the months go by like dust
I feel the trigger of my gun clicking
Every moment,
As I taste the dry crust of my bread
I feel a shiver shivering its way down my spine.
The mud sparks up in the air like a mine . . .

Ben Aidley (9)
Calveley Primary School, Calveley

Royal Wedding

R oyal wedding day had been set
O n the 29th April they did marry
Y ears they has spent together
A ll eyes were on the golden couple
L ove shone throughout the day

W estminster Abbey was the place they chose
E very detail was to perfection
D ays like these are worthy to remember
D iana would have been so proud
I am sure one day he will make a fine king
N ext in the line to the throne after Charles
G ood luck William and Kate.

Emily Drinkall (9)
Calveley Primary School, Calveley

Egyptian Poem

Egypt is what this poem is about,
Read some more and you'll find out,
Egypt is in North-East Africa,
And was the home to Cleopatra.
The river flowing through is called the Nile,
But the Egyptians did things that were pretty vile.
When a rich person died, they were made into a mummy,
They removed all their organs and emptied their tummy.
They didn't used words, they used pictures instead,
And wrote about Anubis and the Land of the Dead.
We call that style of writing hieroglyphic,
Even today it still looks terrific.
Pyramids and the sphinx are in Egypt, go see 'em
Or failing that you can go to a museum.

Izzie Moulton (9)
Calveley Primary School, Calveley

Travel Back In Rhyme

They came in their astonishing chariots of fire,
They gave us roads, ovens and money to hire,
Villas built of magnificent splendour,
Mosaics and colours to make them a worthy contender,
Their underfloor heating was second to none,
I would have liked to be present in those days now long gone.

All of the history books are full of their amazing inventions,
Without them there would be no wheel, of detail, to attention,
They protected the land with incredible forts,
Their weapons were made from the earth of all sorts,
They worshipped the gods, Jupiter, Neptune and the Gorgon,
And even Carna, the goddess of vital organs.

Who are these immemorial people, why they are the Romans.

Kate Edge (11)
Calveley Primary School, Calveley

The Blitz

In 1939 the world went mad, a truly strange mix of good and bad,
Bombs and tanks and guns and planes, ships and knives and lots of grenades.
The Blitz went on and on through day and night, both sides believed they had the right,
To flex their muscle, show their might, until the other gave up the fight.
Battles were fought on ground, sea and air, total chaos, mess and confusion everywhere.
Lots of people lost and gave their lives.
In order that our future was secure and we could thrive.
In 1945 the turmoil finally came to an end, and countries once enemies now become friends,
I am grateful for the sacrifices made, but I do hear that there is never any future reason to invade.

Hannah Copeland (10)
Calveley Primary School, Calveley

Olympic Games

The games started in Greece,
And there was no need for police,
Sports men and women trying to do their best,
Each event was a test,
To win bronze, silver and gold,
Athletes brave and bold.
The Olympic flag was chosen in 1920,
Competitions were plenty.
Carrying the flame used to be a race,
Teams were running at a fast pace.
Olympics is happening next year,
And is here to stay, it's clear!

Harry Huntbach (10)
Calveley Primary School, Calveley

Queen Victoria

There was once a little girl called Vic
She was going to give history a bit of a kick.
Alexandra Victoria was her real name
She ruled over England for her long, long reign.
At 18 she was crowned to head England till they frowned.
At 21 Albert she did marry
And it was nine sweet children she did carry.
Oh how she cried when her beloved Albert died
With her dull dresses on she continued her duties with great pride.
Oh how she tried but in 1909 she finally died
Her desire and hunger is there to be seen
God save our gracious Queen.

Charlotte Kinsey (9)
Calveley Primary School, Calveley

The Tudors

The Tudors ruled England and Wales for over one hundred years,
The first Tudor king was Henry the VII, who was followed by Henry the VIII,
Henry the VIII had six wives
And the first was Catherine of Aragon who was divorced,
The second was Anne Boleyn who was beheaded,
The third was Jane Seymour who died,
The fourth was Anne of Cleves who got divorced,
The fifth was Catherine Howard who was beheaded,
The last was Katherine Parr who surprisingly survived,
And the rhyme of the wives who Henry married goes like this,
Divorced, beheaded, died, divorced, beheaded, survived.

Dominic Wright (10)
Calveley Primary School, Calveley

World War II

World War II was a big, big war
It lasted six long years
Germany cackled as Britain battled
On and on through the day and night

On the battlefield grenades flew like birds
The echo of Tommy guns was in the air
The bullets of Spitfires sent enemy planes to the ground
The atomic bomb dropped, death was all around.

Sam White (10)
Calveley Primary School, Calveley

Cave People

'Ooh!' said Daddy Caveman
'Aar!' said Baby back
'Urgh!' said Mummy Caveman
So Daddy shouted back
'Rarr!' said Grandpa Caveman
To the quivering T-rex
'Ooh arr ug rarrrrr!' said the whole family including Auntie Bex.

Harry Tomlins (10)
Calveley Primary School, Calveley

My Mum . . .

My mum says I am beautiful,
The world didn't look at me,
My mum says I am the best, I didn't know this myself.

My mum thinks I would make her proud,
'Just let the world know who you are.'
My mum thinks I am the one, who she can depend,
I will never let her down.

My mum can feel it is too hard,
I will try until I can.
My mum knows that I am what she wants,
I know I will do my duty.

My mum wishes the world to look at me,
I know I need to find the way,
My mum wishes I fulfil my dreams,
I know one day I will make her proud!

Waheeda Khatun (9)
Heasandford Primary School, Burnley

The Egyptian Poem

Mummies are very old
Although they are very cold.

Mummies are put in tombs
Where it is not like a room.

Where the Egyptians used to dance
Other people stood and glanced.

They used lots of bricks
But the pharaoh used to kick.

In Egypt it was very hot
Although they made clay pots.

Hannah Fish (8)
Heaton Avenue First School, Cleckheaton

The Poem Of Ancient Egypt

Anubis, the god of the dead, the jackal,
Enjoys chatting and having a cackle.
Mummies creeping up and down,
Watch your step, try not to frown.

Pyramids built day and night,
Sometimes their beauty can give you a fright.
Pharaohs all over ruling the world,
Speaking up so they can be heard.

Along the desert lays thick, dry sand,
Jackals howling like a haunted band.
Ancient hieroglyphics written on the wall,
Tales of how the mighty Egyptians fall.

In a dark, cold, quiet room,
Lay Tutankhamen in his tomb.
The River Nile floods once more,
It came rising quick from door to door.

Egyptian slaves working all day,
The pyramids must be built in a certain way.
Isis, Re, Seth and Bes,
All work together to create happiness.

Ashley Evered (8)
Heaton Avenue First School, Cleckheaton

Awesome Egyptians

Making a mummy is not very easy,
Pulling out the brain can make you quite queasy.
Building a pyramid up to the sky,
Most of them are over 100 metres high.
Hieroglyphics is the way they write,
To write that way they must be very bright.

Emily Moran (8)
Heaton Avenue First School, Cleckheaton

World War II

W orld War II started in 1939, September the 3rd at 11am and ended in 1945.
O h how sad the children would have been, leaving their families. They must
   have been so sad getting picked out by a stranger.
R uining cities, homes and lives.
L eaders were strong, Adolf Hitler, Winston Churchill, Neville Chamberlain,
   Roosevelt, Stalin and all.
D ads and other men that were brave enough to be in the war died by bombs
   and guns. The men who didn't fight had another job.

W orld War II started because Hitler was not happy as a result of what
   happened in World War I.
A huge amount of children were taken away from their family during the war.
R apidly fighting and some even declaring more war. Awfully disappointing.

T he war was taking forever, nearly seven years. They couldn't wait any longer,
   they wanted it to stop.
W ar, what is it good for?
O h please stop the war!

Erin Rosendale (9)
Killin Primary School, Killin

World War II

W orld War II began on the third of September 1939.
O nce the war had started children were evacuated
   from the city to the countryside for safety.
R adios were used like the televisions we have now to listen to news
   about events during World War II.
L ong ships were used to go to sea and protect them.
D ecisions were made between all of the different countries
   that fought in World War II.

W inston Churchill became Prime Minister of Great Britain in 1940.
A nderson Shelter was a shelter for protection, if there were any bombs around.
R ussia were allies of Britain and France.

T he war lasted six and a half years.
W ar, war what was it worth?
O h, what was the need for the war?

Hayley Ramsay (9)
Killin Primary School, Killin

World War II Poem

W ar was extremely bad and men went out to fight in the war and some got killed.

O n the 3rd of September, the war began. It finished in 1945.

R adios were used to tell all the people that the war was going to start.

L ots of children were moved to safer places when the war had started. That is called evacuation.

D ifferent countries fought in the war, like Germany, France, America, Poland and Great Britain.

W inston Churchill was involved in World War II. He became the new British Prime Minister in 1940.

A nderson Shelters protected families when the war began. They built them when the war started.

R ussia were great friends with Britain and France.

T he war started because of Hitler and the Nazis.

W ar, war, why did you begin war? War you are so bad.

O n Christmas Day they did play a big game of football.

Megan Pease (11)
Killin Primary School, Killin

World War II

W orld War II started on September in 1939.

O ld people today fought in World War II when they were younger.

R otten people joined World War II.

L adies were not safe as they stayed in the city.

D angerous places at war such as Poland, Germany, Romania, UK, France, Spain, Sweden, Norway and Japan and America.

W rong choices were made by Adolf Hitler.

A dolf Hitler came to power because everybody agreed with his idea to help Germany.

R ifles were used in World War II.

T errible things happened such as people were killed, families were killed and children were killed.

W inston Churchill was Prime Minister in 1940.

O h why can't they get along?

Ben McLarty (10)
Killin Primary School, Killin

World War II

W orld War II started in 1939 and so many people were devastated.
O n the 3rd of September World War II was officially declared.
R eally brave men joined the army to fight for their country.
L oving families got the call of death.
D eath was around the corner for lots of soldiers and you were very lucky if you
lived.

W orried soldiers didn't know if they would see their families again.
A ngry Adolf Hitler lead the Nazi party to fight.
R ifles, guns, bombs and grenades were used in World War II as weapons.

T errified children made their way to their new homes.
W inston Churchill became Prime Minister of Britain in 1940.
O nly children were evacuated and were taken to the countryside, where it was
thought to be safe.

Amy Forster (9)
Killin Primary School, Killin

WWII Poem!

W orld War started on the 3rd September 1939.
O nly evacuees were safe in WWII because women had to stay in the city.
R evolting war was faced by brave soldiers.
L adies were not safe because war was in lots of cities all over the world.
D readful results for soldiers and women's lives as thousands of them were
killed.

W ar, war, what was it worth?
A nderson Shelters protected families from bomb attacks.
R ation books were back in WWII to get families food.

T anks are great weapons for war because they are big machines which means
less of your country being killed.
W inston Churchill became Prime Minister of Great Britain in 1940.
O h, why couldn't they not just get along?

Beth Allan (10)
Killin Primary School, Killin

WWII Poem

W oeful memories still fill the hearts of people of that awful day,
O n the 3rd of September 1939,
R ough lives for soldiers when they fought for their countries,
L eaving families behind meant broken hearts and floods of tears,
D eath of loved ones was a constant worry to all,

W omen from the city let their husbands go to war,
A gony as they sent children away to the safety of the countryside,
R uthless Nazis destroyed everything they could on Adolf Hitler's commands.

T errible Hitler struck fear into innocent hearts,
W ar left many broken hearted,
O nly these were the days when the war had just started. There were six more
years of tears to come.

Hazel Lafferty (11)
Killin Primary School, Killin

World War II Poem

W hen war started in 1939, there was a lot of devastation,
O ver the days at the start of the war the brave soldiers risked their lives for their
countries,
R adios announced that war was declared,
L ives were lost, houses were lost and cities were destroyed,
D etermined to take over other countries Adolf Hitler lead the Nazi party to war,

W inston Churchill became Prime Minister of Great Britain in 1940,
A ll the children in big cities were evacuated and taken to the countryside,
R ussia, France and Great Britain were allies.

T he war went on until the year 1945,
'W ar, war, what is it good for?'
'O f course we will win, we'll win for sure!'

Annie Chisholm (10)
Killin Primary School, Killin

World War II

W orld War II had come it was the 3rd of September 1939
' O f course we were sad but we had to fight for our country!'
R ight away thousands of men across Britain signed up for the oncoming war.
' L oud noises, all night, I just can't sleep.'
' D o I have to go?' all the children cried as they were taken from their families.

'W ould it ever end?'
A ll countries involved were listening on the radio as new leaders came to power.
R apidly, death numbers rose high.

' T o war!'
'W e know we can win!'
'O f course we can!'

Stuart Lang (11)
Killin Primary School, Killin

World War II

W orld War II started as a consequence of gruesome World War I,
O n 2/9/39, Hitler declared war,
R ampaging through villages, towns and cities, killing anyone they found,
L ives of children saved by evacuation,
D ecoding what to do, the Prime Minister really struggled with this,

W inston Churchill became Prime Minister of the UK in 1940,
A rmies were big and getting bigger all the time,
R aiding, searching and wrecking things with bombs and guns, Germany were merciless,

T hen along came Britain, France and America,
W ere things going to change?
O h I wish there were no wars between countries.

Jack Robinson (9)
Killin Primary School, Killin

45

WWII

W hy did the war begin?
O h how many more lives?
R apid fire everywhere
L ives in ruins everywhere
D eath everywhere by guns.

W ho lurks, causing lots of danger.
A new home for children.
R ifles were made for danger.

T oday don't have world wars.
W e didn't flee.
O h, we will win.

Tyler Montgomery-Windsor (9)
Killin Primary School, Killin

World War II

W ar began on September the 3rd.
O nly children were evacuated.
R adios were used to tell people what was going on.
L ives were saved but many lost.
D eath was scattered all over the world.

W riting letters to family was not a joy.
A nderson Shelters were used to protect people from bombs.
R ough soldiers fought in the war.

T omorrow I want the war to end,
W ar seems like it will never end.
O nly if someone brave enough would stop the war.

Bethany Semple (9)
Killin Primary School, Killin

World War II

W orld War II started on September the 3rd in Poland.
' O h, what a gruesome start to the war.'
R adios were used to announce news.
L ots of families broken by Germany.
D anger was everywhere in cities and sometimes in the countryside.

'W ar, how long is it going to be?'
A llies are our friends and we fought with them.
R ed, blue and white is the colour of our flag.

T his is how it started.
W orld War II started because of Germany.
O h, how many soldiers were killed?

Noah Robinson (8)
Killin Primary School, Killin

World War II

W orld War II began in 1939.
O n Sunday the 3rd of September the World War began.
R adios were saying the war was beginning.
L ots of lives were lost in the war.
D eath was getting closer and closer to soldiers.

W orrying soldiers were scared that they might not see their families
A ll the children went on a train and got new families.
R ussia, France and Great Britain were all friends.

T omorrow I want to go home.
W indows were blacked out so nobody could see them.
O nly children were evacuated, not women or men.

Emily Fraser (9)
Killin Primary School, Killin

47

WWII

W ar has broken out because of Hitler.
O n the 3rd of September war broke out.
R adios were telling the news of the war.
L earning children leaving their parents.
D eath reports everywhere.

W inston Churchill had taken charge in the forties.
A nderson Shelters were being used more often.
R ations were no help if you had 12 children.

T rains were used for evacuees.
W riting letters to people in the war was upsetting.
O n the second year people had their fingers crossed the war would end soon.

Eloise Murray (9)
Killin Primary School, Killin

Travel Back In Rhyme

The Romans and Saxons all warriors brave,
Were willing to battle right to their grave.
Swords and shields were carried proud,
Their battle cries they shouted loud.
The Bayeux Tapestry reveals a lot,
When through the eye Harold got shot.
Julius Caesar was a clever geezer,
He was the Roman's leader.
But from these days we have a lot to remember,
Our predecessors were great inventors,
Toothpaste, sausage, tunnels and soap,
Canals and arched bridges gave us future hope.
We use them all every day,
A big *thank you* we'd like to say.

Jordan Taylor (10)
Lordsgate Township CE Primary School, Burscough

A Gory Story

In a haunted house at ten at night,
Two angry ghosts got up to fight!
One was called Creeper one was called Crawl,
And Creeper pushed Crawl,
So he banged his head against the wall!
So that meant obviously Creeper had won,
Unless Crawl took a gun,
And that's the first verse done!

The ghosts didn't actually know they were dead,
Until Creeper shot Crawl right in the head!
The rest of the details are very gory
So I am not going to tell you the full story!

Lewis James (10)
Lordsgate Township CE Primary School, Burscough

One, Two, Three, Fight!

I was sailing on my boat,
I forgot to bring my coat,
Bang! There's one more gone,
Mind, there's a bomb,
The spike digs right in,
Be careful, there's a pin,
The whistle is blown 'Final round,'
Another is down on the ground,
Punch! Punch! Punch, right in the face,
It is the end, everyone goes at a slow pace.

Sophie Ponsonby (10)
Lordsgate Township CE Primary School, Burscough

Egypt Poem

I saw a golden pyramid shining in the light
A golden pyramid sharp like a knife
A dark and scary tomb like midnight
The River Nile sparkly blue
Scaly crocodiles with teeth like blades

I heard mummies groaning like lions
Snapping crocodiles munching all the fish
Tomb robbers smashing through walls
Wind whistling through the air and
Cracking bricks breaking off pyramids

I felt sticky cobwebs on a dusty tomb
A fierce wind beating on me
The sun as hot as fire burning and
Mummies grabbing me.

Josh Henderson (8)
Lumphinnans Primary School, Lumphinnans

Egyptian Poem

Golden pyramids sharp as a knife
The monstrous pyramid is blazing in the sun
I saw a mummy racing to his tomb
The tunnel was so very narrow

An enormous camel riding on the golden sand
The sun so bright it was blinding
The River Nile is so sparkly and blue
Crocodiles so fierce and scary, they make me want to run away

The River Nile flowing gently in the wind as
Crocodiles snap their teeth
Sand swirling around the pyramids
Mummies groaning in their sarcophagi
Feel the sticky cobwebs as the pyramid bricks begin to crumble.

Rhiannon Herd (8)
Lumphinnans Primary School, Lumphinnans

Egyptian Poem

Monstrous pyramid
A pyramid as sharp as a knife
The blazing hot sand
A sun that is boiling hot
A fierce crocodile in the blue River Nile.

A camel as red as the sun
The roasting hot ancient Egyptian desert
The sparkly Nile so bright it blinds you
Crocodiles munching day and night.

Burglars breaking into tombs
Mummies with red eyes as bright as the moon
Mummies breaking pyramid bricks
Mummies groaning and giving everyone a fright.

Finlay Moffat (8)
Lumphinnans Primary School, Lumphinnans

Egyptian Poem

I can see a giant tomb with a tiny cave
The River Nile splashing and a big crocodile snapping
I can see Cleopatra with a beautiful smile
Sand swirling around a giant pyramid.

I can hear a mummy groaning
And servants screaming
Waves splashing on the River Nile and crocodiles munching
I can feel the sand burning my feet
And sand across the walls of the tomb.

Declan Clark (8)
Lumphinnans Primary School, Lumphinnans

Egyptian Poem

A golden, sandy desert with sand as soft as a feather.
A mummy as white as a sheet
And as big as a pharaoh.
A big, golden, sharp pyramid with a little entrance.
The River Nile is blue and has crocodiles with teeth like razors.

The sound of animals drinking water.
Pyramids cracking and crumbling in the sand.
Mummies groaning in their tombs.
Sand storms howling all around.

Connie Templeman (8)
Lumphinnans Primary School, Lumphinnans

Egyptian Poem

I saw a golden triangle pyramid with a tiny tunnel.
A yellow desert with sand like feathers.
The bright sun was shining hot upon my back.
The long River Nile was blue like the sky
And filled with sharp toothed crocodiles.

I heard the River Nile flowing gently in the wind.
Crocodiles snapping their teeth at fish swimming past.
Mummies groaning in their sarcophagi.
Sand hitting off the pyramids.

Molly Bernard (8)
Lumphinnans Primary School, Lumphinnans

Egyptian Poem

Go back three thousand years to an ancient Egyptian land.
The sand so soft, softer than a cuddly toy.
Cleopatra next to a bright red camel wearing lovely jewellery at the River Nile.
A monstrous pyramid with a microscopic tunnel and an enormous, golden shiny sarcophagus.

You can hear the sound of the gentle flowing River Nile.
And the jaw-dropping crocodiles eating the squirming fish.
Mummies moaning and knocking on the pyramid walls, trying to get out.
Sand swirling like a tornado, as loud as a siren.

Eve Catherine Stewart (8)
Lumphinnans Primary School, Lumphinnans

Egyptian Poem

In the River Nile are snapping crocodiles with teeth
like razor blades.
Enormous pyramids like knife tops.
A sarcophagus inside a very dark tomb with tiny tunnels.
In the tiny tunnels I stumbled over a rock.
Then I felt a cobweb over my face, it was sticky.
Some swirling sand came around my feet,
Then I was burning hot.
Then a mummy was touching me.

Carlie Sneddon (8)
Lumphinnans Primary School, Lumphinnans

Scotland

S cotland is beautiful!
C airns are seen and built on top of hills.
O ' bonnie Scotland I love the best!
T o A Mouse is one of Robert Burn's famous poems.
L och Ness is where Nessie is supposed to live!
A ndy Cameron is a famous Scottish singer
N orthern lights dance across the sky!
D ancing the highland fling is a tradition in Scotland.

Katrina MacKay (10)
Melvich Primary School, Melvich

Dinosaur Time

Dinosaurs ruled the Earth
Sixty million years ago
They ruled the sea and land
If you want to see them
Travel back to dinosaur time
But if you do – *watch out*
T-rex might eat you!

Rebecca Howie (9)
Netherton Northside First School, Morpeth

Romans

R ome was their home
O ff they went to roam
M aking roads all over Britain
A ttacked by the Scots
N orthumbrians they defeated
S oldiers carrying swords.

Thomas Johnston (8)
Netherton Northside First School, Morpeth

A Pilot In The Battle Of Britain

I could see bullets flying past me.
There was black smoke in the air.
I saw exploded petrol pumps.
I could see houses on fire.

I could hear bombs being dropped.
I could hear guns firing.
I could hear people screaming.
I could hear other planes going past.

I feel worried and scared.
Sometimes I feel like screaming.
I am always cold.
I feel angry because I don't like being too high up in the air.

Chloe Leask (9)
Olnafirth Primary School, Shetland Islands

A Pilot In The Battle Of Britain

Many bombs explode as I fly over Britain, it is upsetting.
I wish Hitler would pay for the disgrace he has done.
My wife and son have died, I hate all this.
Bullets flying past through my cockpit, I'm crying because
it's so frightening.

I hear the screams of the planes, darting to the ground.
And listen to the explosion, there's nothing left of the Spitfire.
I hear my best mate hit on the radio, there's nothing worth
living for.
My conscience tells me I must not give up.

I see smoke drifting from the shot down planes.
Young German pilots flying their Messerschmitt planes.
I take aim through my sights, oh no my guns are jammed!
A bullet penetrates my engine, this is the end.

Edward Hallam (10)
Olnafirth Primary School, Shetland Islands

A Pilot In The Battle Of Britain

Planes diving out of the sky.
Bombs exploding with great power.
People waving their arms and cheering us on.
Shrapnel bouncing off the planes.

Hear the people crying.
Exploding bombs that deafen me.
The gun shots of the people helping from below.
Your captain talking to you in the rear.

Feel the anger that tenses your muscles.
The recoil of the machine gun.
The adrenaline running through my veins.
Black smoke filling my lungs.

Lewis Hall (11)
Olnafirth Primary School, Shetland Islands

A Pilot In The Battle Of Britain

I can hear loud explosions
Rat-a-tat machine guns firing
Churchill roaring, 'We're gonna win!'
Plane engines going *nnnnnnnnnn*

I feel exhausted and tired
I feel the anger inside
I feel scared I might die
I feel excited to defend my country

I see black smoke out of the window
I can see planes crashing to the ground
I can see German planes shooting at me
I can see lots of fields below.

Jack Garrick (9)
Olnafirth Primary School, Shetland Islands

Scary Pirate Island

What can you see?
Pirates running through the street with smelly feet shouting,
'I won the fight,'
Pirates snoring, swaying on their hammock in the rough sea,
The pirates singing but they are trying to bomb us,
Pirates screaming because they are being hanged by their head on rope,
Hanged from the edge of the boat.

What can you feel?
I have nerves in my body,
I can feel butterflies in my tummy,
Shivers going up my body and spine,
I can feel knives going through my body.

What can you hear?
Pistols banging as they fight,
People singing in the street,
People screaming,
People shouting.

Courtney Davis (8)
Park Primary School, Stranraer

The Evil Pirate Crew

What can you see?
Pirates hiding behind barrels because guns are going off,
Glittering treasure and shining sand on the island,
Pirates putting a shining cutlass through another pirate's chest,
A big black and white flag flapping in the air
With a cross bone on it.

What can you feel?
Seasick from the big heavy sea waves,
A big scary parrot tickling my shoulder while sailing the boat,
A cutlass hitting my shoulder and guns shooting me in the back,
The breeze of the wind hitting me.

What can you hear?
Cutlass banging off of the boat in a fight,
Barrels rolling along the shining brown boat,
Pirates yelling on the boat because other pirates are
Coming to fight them,
Pirates hitting each other in a big huge fight.

Emily Kane (8)
Park Primary School, Stranraer

The Pirate Ship

What can you see?
An old wrecked pirate ship at the bottom of the sea,
No sailor to be seen,
There is a flickering mast with an old torn sail and an old window,
There are pirates drinking rum by the clock, could they be drunk?
Pirates shooting pistols at one another.

What can you hear?
Pirates yelling at everyone on the ship,
People are snoring on the ship,
Pirates are fighting with shiny daggers and cutlass,
People are fighting fearlessly at the dock.

What can you feel?
The pirate feels old and dirty,
He feels sore and dizzy,
Weird and gross,
Cold and lonely.

Stuart Whan (8)
Park Primary School, Stranraer

On The Rocky Boat

What can you see?
The pirates with their pistols fighting with other pirates,
A pirate's boat in the middle of the ocean,
I can see treasure buried,
The boat is banging off the rocks.

What can you feel?
I can feel blood running down my body,
A big piece of wood,
An old rusty pirate hat,
Bullet in my body.

What can you hear?
Parrots squawking when the pirates are fighting,
They are having a party, pirates are eating nuts,
The sea splashing.

Chloe Kenneavy (7)
Park Primary School, Stranraer

Pirate Island

What can you see?
There is a blue and red parrot sitting on a pirate's shoulder,
There is a big ugly pirate,
There is a big pirate ship with a Skull and Crossbones,
I see a pirate with a shiny pistol.

What can you feel?
A big shiny cutlass going through me,
There is a shiny pistol in my hand,
I feel a pirate's beard, it's jaggy,
I walk on the island sand, it burns my feet.

What can you hear?
I hear a sword clenching,
There is a noisy parrot that always squawks,
I hear a pistol go off, I am scared,
There are a lot of pirates shouting.

Taylor Le-Texier (8)
Park Primary School, Stranraer

The Rocky Island

What can you see?
The waves hitting off the boat,
The gold sand glittering in the sun,
All the palm trees blowing through the sky,
The rain hitting the sand, it's sticking to our feet.

What can you feel?
I feel scared because other pirates are on the way,
I feel wind hitting off my face,
I feel my hands shaking,
I feel blood dripping down my face.

What can you hear?
The parrots squawking,
The pirate's footsteps,
The palm trees blowing through the sky,
The sand is crunching.

Amiee McDonald (7)
Park Primary School, Stranraer

Treasure Chest

What can you see?
I see lots of shiny and pretty things in the treasure chest,
Down on the pirate ship at the bottom of the sea,
Sparkling jewels shining from the sun,
A big hole in the sand from the treasure.

What can you hear?
The pirate saying, 'There's the treasure,'
The pirate saying, 'Ahoy,'
Pirates talking about treasure,
The gold coins rubbing together.

What can you feel?
The pain when the sword stabs me,
I feel terrified,
The gold running through my fingers,
I feel excited.

Nadia Alexander (8)
Park Primary School, Stranraer

The Treasure Map

What can you see?
The treasure map has a big red cross,
The island ahead is golden sand,
You can see the map is old, yuck,
Can you see a boat in the sea?

What can you feel?
A map that has mud on it,
A gun shooting me,
I feel sad,
I feel scared.

What can you hear?
A gun going off, it's loud,
Pirates shouting, 'Where is the map?'
You hear me in the dark,
Pirates telling stories in the dark.

Nicol Govan (9)
Park Primary School, Stranraer

The Pirates

What can you see?
Pirates shouting as loud as they can,
A boat sailing in the ocean,
Pirates fighting with their daggers,
Pirates with parrots on their shoulders.

What can you feel?
I can feel a boat and pirates stomping their feet,
I feel seasick from the big heavy waves,
I feel blood running down my face,
I feel sore and scared.

What can you hear?
Pirates snoring in the boat,
Pirates fighting, some have died,
I can hear noise from far away,
The pirates are shouting at the captain to steer the wheel the other way.

Bethany Murray (7)
Park Primary School, Stranraer

Aboard A Rocky Pirate Ship

What can you see?
Silver daggers
Ugly pirates with patches and a wooden leg,
Glittery sand shimmering on the island,
Parrots perched on pirates' shoulders.

What can you hear?
Waves splashing and bashing the ship,
Guns going off,
Pirates shouting,
The tropical leaves crunching.

What can you feel?
The pain of getting stabbed in the chest,
The pain of getting killed,
Pirates stomping to come and attack,
My heart is pounding because I feel terrified.

Ellie-Anna Burns (8)
Park Primary School, Stranraer

61

William Shakespeare

What can you see?
Jazzy music playing as I walk down the gloomy, dark alleyway,
Women in frilly frocks itching rapidly,
Susanna, my daughter, dancing gracefully in the glistening sunlight,
Autumn leaves falling all around.

I'm walking into my dream,
My theatre, the Globe,
Men in frilly frocks, red lipstick smudged on their cheeks,
The play begins and my heart thuds, thuds, thuds in my chest.

Subsequently I walk down the open street,
Suddenly a window rapidly flies open,
And in a flash a bucket of icy cold, dirty water pours down
my spine and my hair gets horribly drizzled.

Concentrating on my script,
Sitting in my study,
Romeo meets Juliet and the story excitedly evolves.

What can you hear?
I hear the cry of the actors in my mind,
As I write my play when Juliet dies,
Sadly, because she poisoned herself,
'Oh my.'

The scratch, scratch, scratch of my feathery pen,
Splashing in the ink,
ferociously clashing on the paper.
Constant clapping as the actors play their roles,
My stomach tightly clenched,
Scared if the crowd will want more.

The tuneful music played on a wooden recorder as I saunter down the old,
cobbled street
And the flames as a strange looking minstrel throws hot fire up into the bright,
sunny sky
As the crowd anxiously wait for a mistake to take place.

What can you feel?
The spittle in my dry throat as I am fed putrid pottage.
The spikes of the spindly straw beneath my bare feet.
I feel the contrast between the soft down of the feather and the harsh pointed nib of my quill.
My beloved Anne's velvety gown brushes briefly against my blushing cheek.

Olivia Middlehurst (10)
Pendle Primary School, Clitheroe

A Roman Soldier

What can you see?
Charging chariots chasing down the enemy, spikes coming out of the wheels, chopping them down,
Celts with bright blue paint all over their strong bodies, including frightening people with spiky spears charging towards us.
My helpless friends slaughtered by the cruel and menacing Celts with no mercy at all.
Romans walking mournfully back to camp after the loss of a battle to Boudicca's boisterous army.

What can you hear?
Battle cries of the marching Celts tearing at my weak ears, wanting to make them fall off onto the blood-stained ground.
Orders of our centurion, telling us where to go and swatting at invisible flies in the air.
Pleading friends, tearing at my ankles, telling me to take them back to our camp with them.
Cries of joy from the Romans as we finally capture Boudicca but then moans as she kills herself.

What can you feel?
The water flooding into my ancient boots making them heavier and heavier by each painful step.
My shield clashing with others as we make the famous battle tactic, the tortoise.
A horrible headache from the noise of slashing swords, clashing with one another in the sunlight.
The agony from a terrible wound on the back of my limping leg, formed by an arrow.

James Baird (10)
Pendle Primary School, Clitheroe

63

A Roman Traitor

What can you see?

The ruthless Roman soldiers chasing me, desperate to catch me before I spill
out any more hurtful information.
But I must, no I must not be caught.
I see the purple panther I just dangerously disturbed and the frondy ferns
flapping in the gentle breeze.
A water plant and another, stranger sort.
There's the cruel rocky path from which I often have to stray,
And I see there in the distance the hard, hostile castle that I have to reach for my
laden life depends on it.

What can you hear?

The sudden screams of merciless men as I leap out
and kill them to get off my trail.
But as I look down at them my heart fills with a fearful,
ferocious pity.
I hear thunder crashing as it darkens the wild sky.
The clouds in the shape of the Emperor's face leering, laughing
out at me.
But it does nothing but make me wonder.
There are victorious villains thrilling as they take from an
unknowing wanderer,
Before it turns to disastrous dismay as I take it from them.

What can you feel?

I feel pity and dismay, cruelty and fear.
My heart fills with tears of agony as emotion strikes me.
As I step down the dusty road, so sandy it is like the beach.
I feel horror and dread creeping up me,
And I vaguely remember pain, tiredness overwhelming me, then I collapse and
think no more.

Charlotte Wood (9)
Pendle Primary School, Clitheroe

A Shakespeare Actor

What can you see?

I can see the other actors getting ready, feeling the horrible itchiness of their costumes for the first time.

I see myself looking hideous in a horrible, itchy lady's gown, decorated with jewels galore.

I see my character Elizabeth preparing herself to die a horrible, horrible death.

I see the audience clapping and cheering but soon their happy mood will change to booing, dreadful, dreadful booing.

What can you hear?

I can hear the highs and lows of my voice

I can hear my gown rustling slightly every time I move

I can hear the director giving out bossy orders here and there.

I can hear the other actors singing a beautiful, beautiful song.

What can you feel?

I feel nervous because I do not want to forget my lines.

I feel irritated for I always have to act a stupid girl!

I feel glad as this play is over, peace at last!

I feel happy as I wriggle out of my horrible, itchy ladies gown and pull on my own comfy clothes.

Rhianydd Sword (10)
Pendle Primary School, Clitheroe

A Viking Invader

What can you see?

I can see our men savagely slaughtering innocent monks in their huge monasteries.
Our men ransacking all the wealth from inside the monasteries,
whilst monks pray to their god for protection.
Ginormous longboats landing on the rocky shore and men jumping down to join the battle,
their blood-stained swords shimmering in the glowing sunlight.
Fire burning fiercely inside the tiny straw huts that contain screaming children,
realising the fate that waits in store for them.

What can you hear?

I can hear the clashing of swords pinging off the enemy's shields.
I can hear the shrill cries of soldiers as they fall dead or fatally wounded.
The waves crashing violently into the huge, rocky cliffs.
The evil fire crackling like an evil demon inside the houses that once stood.

What can you feel?

I can feel the sense of victory as we drink from our enemy's skulls.
The sense of happiness as I know I will return home a hero.
My friend's hands patting me on the back because we have won.
Then cold metal as it pierces through my back,
only too late do I realise we have been caught in an ambush
I can see my friends flop dead then I breathe my final breath.

Sam Mulligan (11)
Pendle Primary School, Clitheroe

66

Queen Cleopatra

What can you see?

Servants scurrying around like mice reaping the harvest.

Slaves working all around me, trying to please me for their lives.

The Nile flooding, children trying to run away from it.

A pyramid building almost beckoning me to my doom.

What can you hear?

The scarab beetle scurrying frantically across the desert sands.

Slaves clanking their tools, building palaces and tombs.

My conscience telling me to murder myself while I can.

A venomous snake hissing contentedly after his meal of mice and rats.

What can you feel?

The boiling sand between my dainty toes.

Silk around my body as I walk aimlessly around my beautiful golden palace.

Sadness flooding my body as I realise it's time to say goodbye to Cleopatra.

A venomous snake's teeth stabbing into my arm and the venom flowing through my body.

Amy Green (10)
Pendle Primary School, Clitheroe

A Roman Soldier

What can you see?

Millions of Celts marching up the hill aggressively.
Spears zooming through the air, slicing and slaughtering.
Celts on rampage running and screaming wildly.
Horses galloping energetically while the rider kills.

What can you hear?

Screams of useless soldiers painfully limping.
Centurions screaming energetically at the weak soldiers.
Swords and shields clashing and clanging together noisily.
Children running away from their houses, burning letting off a ghastly smell.

What do you feel?

Blood dripping down my forehead sending a shiver up my back.
Pain after being shot, sadly in the leg.
Pain in my heart after all my friends, injured or dead.
Helpless and dead soaked in mud, I am over.

Oscar Howard (10)
Pendle Primary School, Clitheroe

The Evacuee

I see the children sobbing with their parents,
I see the train with lots of smoke.
The teachers shouting out numbers,
And the children boarding the train.

I hear the engine of the train,
And the children refusing and shouting.
I hear the shallow singing,
And the footsteps as they begin their journey.

I feel the wind and the rain beating against me,
And the confusion in my brain.
I feel unwanted and alone,
I am the evacuee.

Daniel Menzies (11)
Pitcorthie Primary School, Dunfermline

The Evacuee

I see my friends filing into the train,
I see the mothers waving farewell.
Everyone is crying around me,
Children sitting in sadness.

I hear the warden close the doors,
The wind hammering the train.
I hear teachers talking in the distance,
The train squeaks as it grinds to a halt.

I feel the rain trickling down my face,
The pushing of frantic children.
I feel the fear all around me,
But that does not compare to the sadness.

I now know that they were helping me,
Taking me to safety.
I am number 13610,
I am the evacuee.

Iain Brown (11)
Pitcorthie Primary School, Dunfermline

69

The Evacuee

I see infants looking confused.
I see faces of children and parents.
Beloved families waving goodbye,
As the evacuees set off into the distance.

I hear branches bashing against the window,
The children's hearts beating with fear.
I hear stomachs rumbling with starvation,
I hear train wheels trundling along the tracks.

I feel disowned and uncomfortable,
I feel shocked and nervous.
I feel my new father welcoming me in,
I feel terrified of what my new family is like.

I am number 796799,
Hope is heading my way.
Thank you for taking me in,
I am the evacuee.

Nicole McIntosh (11)
Pitcorthie Primary School, Dunfermline

In World War II

In World War II the fighting was due.
People were injured and killed too!
I bet you're glad it wasn't you?

As the men in tanks came to the frontier,
Their faces full of fear.
It all became clear that the fighting was near.

The first gun fired and soon the two sides,
One in khaki, one in grey had mixed together,
The war had started today!

Let's hope that we don't have a World War III
We never know just wait and see.
If we do, it won't be me fighting,
No definitely not me!

Caitlin Baxter (9)
Prenton Preparatory School, Prenton

Cleopatra

C harming great men with such beauty,
L ittle Cleo was such a cutey.
E laborate in heavy make-up and flowing dresses,
O h she was in all the caresses.
P lanning to rule the whole of the land.
A ll the men followed in a band,
T rying to win her hand in marriage.
R uling Egypt with all her might,
A lways ready to put up a fight.

O nly standing to put her rights.
N ever left out in the light.

T rue royalty was shown.
H ero Mark Anthony shared her throne.
E bony black, braided hair.

C overed in gold and jewels.
O h Queen Cleopatra rules.
U ntil she was bitten by an asp.
C ruelly bit her with a great gasp.
H er reign over Egypt was at an end at last.

Easwari Joel (9)
Prenton Preparatory School, Prenton

King Henry The VIII

Divorced, beheaded, died,
Divorced, beheaded, survived.
He was Henry the VIII, he had six sorry wives,
Some say he ruined their lives.

First was Kate of Aragon of course,
Then in their lives there came a divorce.

Last of his wives was Catherine Parr,
In her life she got far.
She survived,
Because Henry died.
And that's the end – ta-ta.

Molly Weir (10)
Prenton Preparatory School, Prenton

71

My Poem

I have a friend that's furious
I have a friend that's glorious
I have a friend and he's a Roman

My friend has got a friend that lives in a tomb
My friend has got a friend that said, 'I'll see you soon'
My friend has got a friend and it's a mummy

My brother has got a friend that has no hand; he lost it in the
First World War
My brother has got a friend and he always feels sore
My brother has got a friend and he is a soldier

My mum has got a friend; he drives her round the bend
My mum has got a friend, he's got six wives, and it never ends!
My mum has got a friend and his name is Henry VIII

My dad has got a friend, she puts wee on her hair so it goes yellow
My dad has got a friend she can get loads of money just by saying hello?
My dad has got a friend and she's Queen Elizabeth!

Elle Nudd (9)
Prenton Preparatory School, Prenton

World War II

It was a cold say,
But it was May!
Air raid sirens on,
But it did not know what was going on.
The sound of planes filled the sky,
Which was pale grey.
I wished it was not May.

Jake Shepherd (9)
Prenton Preparatory School, Prenton

History

We all came in and sat down,
And on our faces was a frown.
Then we started to write out,
Something the teacher was talking about.

Then I started to get involved,
And all my answers were resolved.
Then about Egypt we had a test,
And I turned out to be the best!

We learned about the ancient features,
And then we looked at our teachers.
We looked at the desert and saw all the sand,
I wish I could hold it in my hand.

Who knew history could be so exciting!
I nearly couldn't stop writing.
The rest of the day is a mystery,
But when the bell goes that lesson is history.

Layla Livesey (9)
Prenton Preparatory School, Prenton

The Greeks

The Greeks were excellent people,
Always with the gods so lethal,
Living in their city states,
Each one having their own hates.
Athens, Sparta and Corinth too,
Just to name a few.

Harry Jones (9)
Prenton Preparatory School, Prenton

The Evacuees

They scatter,
They run,
They put their gas masks on,
They are so brave.

They get on the train,
They squeal and scream,
They are petrified because of bombs,
They hear the terrible noise of guns.

They are . . .
The evacuees.

Loren Bibby (9)
St Anne's RC Primary School, Birkenhead

Sibilant Medusa

Hissing snakes
Tempt me to look

My heart racing
My brain banging

Once was a pretty princess – now an ugly beast
Cruel thoughts of turning you to stone
Upon your eyes shall feast

Now dead
I've got your head!

Natasha Marie Mole (9)
St Anne's RC Primary School, Birkenhead

World War II

You can hear machine guns shooting up in the air
You can hear tanks getting blown up by rocket launchers
People getting destroyed
Families don't know what to do
Because they're puzzled and scared.

Jack Brown (9)
St Anne's RC Primary School, Birkenhead

Rich Victorian Lady

Fancy dresses on me,
Hair done very neatly,
Fancy jewellery on me,
Ladies saying, 'Do you want your hair like this?'
I live in a mansion,
I feel people doing my hair
My child playing on a rocking horse,
Teddies on her bed,
Dog in living room barking,
Wind coming from a fan.

Kaci Penhaligon (9)
St Anne's RC Primary School, Birkenhead

World War II

They fight for their lives
They use sharp knives
Guns blasting away
The smell of burning all day
People really injured
People working hard
People every day getting sent loads of food and cards
The war is an extremely dangerous place
Where people try their very best.

Ryan Woodhall (9)
St Anne's RC Primary School, Birkenhead

Rich Lady

Dressed in fancy clothing
Hair done, very fashionable
Fancy jewellery on my neck and wrist
I feel like the richest person on Earth

But when I went poor
I had nothing at all,
Where had all my dresses gone?

Ayesha Fraser (9)
St Anne's RC Primary School, Birkenhead

Napoleon Bonaparte

(15th August 1769 – 5th May 1821)

After the French Revolution of 1789 had overthrown King Louis XVI, Napoleon rose to power rapidly - he was a military genius with a brilliant command.

He was a short man, with the nickname 'the little corporal'. His rise to power was helped by his first wife, the beautiful Josephine de Beauharnais.

After bringing economic prosperity and peace to France, Napoleon set out to conquer the remainder of Europe. He was able to conquer a significant amount of land.

In 1804 Napoleon crowned himself emperor of the French and received the Pope's blessing.

Today Napoleon has a chess move named after him: the 'Napoleon Opening'.

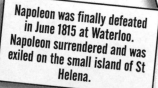

Napoleon was finally defeated in June 1815 at Waterloo. Napoleon surrendered and was exiled on the small island of St Helena.

Joan of Arc
(1412 – 30th May 1431)

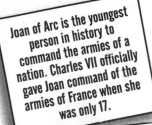

Joan of Arc is the youngest person in history to command the armies of a nation. Charles VII officially gave Joan command of the armies of France when she was only 17.

A prophecy foretold that France would be saved by a maid from Lorraine. It was a popular prediction in France during Joan's time and has been attributed to prophets including the mythical Merlin.

Joan of Arc's greatest military victory was at Patay on June 18th, 1429. Joan's army annihilated the English force, killing over 2,000 while suffering almost no losses.

Charles himself drew Joan's coat of arms featuring a sword holding a crown with a fleur-de-lis on each side.

Joan predicted she would be wounded by an arrow in her chest during an attack on the fort Les Tourelles. Her prediction came true and is documented in a letter written by Charles' cousin fifteen days before.

Joan of Arc was officially canonized by Pope Benedict XV on May 16th 1920, under the same church that executed her for heresy.

Vikings
(The late 8th to the mid 11th century)

The name 'Viking' means 'a pirate raid' in the Old Norse language.

The Vikings were famous for sailing huge distances. Around 500 years before Christopher Columbus 'discovered' the Americas, Vikings had visited their shores. Leif Ericsson was the one who led the Vikings over to what is now Canada in around AD 1000.

Among the many gods Vikings believed in were Thor, the god of thunder, and Loki, a cheeky mischief-maker who could shape-shift to become all different kinds of animals.

The Vikings were expert boat builders and sailors. They invented 'keels' which made their 'longboats' easy to steer, and because of their design to float high in the water, landing on beaches was easy.

Fenrir Greyback, the werewolf in the Harry Potter books, was named after a ferocious giant wolf from Ancient Viking mythology.

Vegetables in Viking times were much smaller than the ones we enjoy today, they were more like wild plants. Viking carrots were dark purple, not orange!

Victorians

(Queen Victoria's reign lasted from 20th June 1837 until her death on 22nd January 1901)

Britain became the most powerful and richest country in the world, with the largest empire that had ever existed, ruling a quarter of the world's population.

Britain built a huge empire during the Victorian period. In 1837 most people lived in villages and worked on the land; by 1901, most lived in towns and worked in offices, shops and factories.

The number of people living in Britain more than doubled from 16 million to 37 million, causing a huge demand for food, clothes and housing.

There were no painkillers nor anaesthesia for the Victorians - operations went on for hours with patients in excruciating agony.

The police force was created during the Victorian period by Sir Robert Peel (hence the nickname 'Bobbies').

To control insects, many people kept a hedgehog in the basement. It curled up and slept in the day, but roamed around the dark kitchen at night eating cockroaches and other insects.

Children were often forced to work. Many were used as cheap labour in factories, or as chimney sweeps. The work was dangerous and painful. Some boys got stuck and died of suffocation.

Henry VIII & Tudors

**(Henry's reign 28th June 1491 – 28th January 1547
Tudor dynasty from 1485 until 1603)**

The first Tudor king was Henry VII. He became king after the Battle of Bosworth Field, which ended the Wars of the Roses.

Henry VIII is probably the most well known of the Tudor monarchs. He was a very selfish person and by the end of his life everyone was afraid of him, mainly because of his ruthless behaviour toward anyone who didn't agree with him.

In 1534, Henry VIII broke away from the Catholic Church and proclaimed himself head of the Church of England. Henry sold off the land and riches of the church to dukes, barons and other noblemen.

Contrary to popular opinion, Henry VIII had many children. Unfortunately it was very common in Tudor times for them to die very young. Only three survived beyond childhood.

An average person drank about 8 pints of 'weak beer' a day. It had very little alcohol in it, and even children drank it. It was safer than the water available at the time.

The ending of the marriages of King Henry VIII can be remembered by the following rhyme:
'Divorced, beheaded, died divorced, beheaded, survived'.

Boudicca

Died between 60 and 62 AD

She was the Queen of the Iceni, an ancient British tribe from East Anglia. When the Romans tried to steal Iceni land and tax the people, Boudicca reportedly raised around 230,000 men to fight against 10,000 Roman soldiers. Somehow the Romans won!

Boudicca, also known as Boudica, Boudiccea or Boudicea, lived nearly 2,000 years ago when Britain was part of the Roman Empire.

The name 'Boudicca' means 'victory'.

Allegedly, when Boudicca realised her army was going to lose the battle, she killed herself by drinking poison, rather than become a Roman prisoner.

A Roman called Dio Cassius described Boudicca as 'tall', 'terrifying', 'fierce', and 'harsh', but also said she was intelligent. He said she had very long, tawny hair and wore a big gold necklace. She also carried a big spear which made her even more scary!

Today, Boudicca, warrior queen of the Iceni, is considered a heroine who stood against the hated Roman invaders. A life-sized statue of her now stands at Westminster Bridge, across from the Houses of Parliament.

Roman Empire

(27 BC – AD 476/1453)

The Romans came to Britain nearly 2000 years ago (43 AD until 410 AD) and changed our country. Even today, evidence of the Romans being here can be seen in the ruins of Roman buildings, forts, roads and baths found all over Britain.

The Romans were responsible for killing many Christians but later they became Christian themselves and the killing stopped.

The Romans were very civilised and their villas had central heating and baths.

Romans loved to make laws, by the end they had written down about 3 million of them. Most of our laws are based on old Roman ones.

In the old Roman calendar there were only 10 months, March was the beginning of the year and there were no months in the winter! The month 'July' is named after the emperor Julius Caesar and 'August' is named after Emperor Augustus.

Pecunia non olet means 'money does not smell'. This phrase was coined as a result of the urine tax charged by the Roman emperors in the 1st century upon the collection of urine. It was used in tanning, and also by launderers as a source of ammonia to clean and whiten woollen togas. There are even isolated reports of it being used as a teeth whitener!

Cleopatra
(69–30 BC)

Cleopatra was a master of 9 languages, and was the only person in the entire Ptolemaic dynasty who could speak Egyptian! Wow!

Cleopatra married 2 of her own brothers, ew!

Historians believe that Cleopatra was not stunningly beautiful, but had an ordinary face with a hooked nose, and 'masculine' features.

Cleopatra wasn't Egyptian; she was Greek.

As Queen, Cleopatra was skilled in the arts of warfare. She was a naval commander, and twice led her fleet in battle.

Cleopatra was extremely charismatic and quick-witted. She was very good at persuading people to do things the way she wanted them.

Cleopatra was 39 years old when she died from the bite of a cobra.

Ancient Egypt
(3150 BC – 30 BC)

Ancient Egyptians had great medical skills. They could set broken bones, perform surgeries, and they even developed anaesthetic.

The Ancient Egyptians developed the toilet seat, combs, scissors, make-up, toothpaste and toothbrushes.

Both men and women in Egypt wore make-up to protect their skin from the hot sun.

The Ancient Egyptians measured one hour as one twelfth of the day between sunrise and sunset. This meant that an hour was much longer in summer than in winter.

Pharaoh Pepi II of Egypt used slaves smeared in honey, to attract flies away from him!

The people of Ancient Egypt divided Egypt into two areas. The 'Red Land' was the deserts that protected both sides of Egypt from neighbouring countries and invading armies. The 'Black Land' was the fertile land near the River Nile where people grew their crops.

Nearly all Ancient Egyptian homes had a cat, but cats were not pets. The Ancient Egyptians believed that cats had magical powers. They believed cats protected their homes and children from danger.

Prehistoric Life

(250 million years ago to about 3200BC)

Prehistoric refers to time preceding both human existence and the invention of writing

At one point, all of the Earth's continents are thought to have been connected as one huge land mass. This one huge 'continent' is known as Pangaea.

Archaeology is the study of past human life and culture by the examination of actual evidence, such as graves, buildings, tools and pottery.

Geology is the study of the origin, history, and structure of the Earth.

The Earth is 4.5 billion years old. It took nearly a billion years for the atmosphere to become stable enough to sustain life.

Palaeontology is the study of fossils of life existing in prehistoric times.

To help fight carnivores, many herbivores had natural weapons at their disposal. Examples of this include the spikes on the tail of the stegosaurus and the three horns attached to the front of the triceratops' head.

The largest tooth of any carnivorous dinosaur found to this date is that of a T-rex. It is estimated to have been around 30cm (12in) long including the root.

The Cretaceous era ended with the mass extinction of the dinosaurs. It's widely believed that an asteroid 6 miles in diameter struck the Earth in the Gulf of Mexico, leaving a crater 150 miles wide.

64 million years after dinosaurs became extinct, humans emerged in the Cenozoic era.

World War II

I watch the soldiers fall to the ground
I can hear the guns hammering, *bang, bang!*
Blood everywhere

The smell of death burns my nose

I look to my left, I see a dead body covered in blood
Vomit and bile rises up my neck.

My friend, Paul, has just been shot.

Holly Ann Dunne (9)
St Anne's RC Primary School, Birkenhead

World War II

In World War II people were thought of as targets
There was blood everywhere.
Blood spraying out of people's legs.
Guns firing, people screaming for help.
Blood all over the grass.
Bombs dropping,
Smoke everywhere,
People with gasmasks on.

Jordan Goodwin (9)
St Anne's RC Primary School, Birkenhead

World War II

Machine gun's spray invades the air,
Bombs exploding when they hit the ground,

People dying, people screaming, blood squirting out of people's heads.
There is a river of blood flowing through the city.

Everybody shouting and crying, people getting shot.

Callum Bennion (9)
St Anne's RC Primary School, Birkenhead

Henry VIII

I see King Henry VIII with his belly like jelly.
I see the jewels on his clothes
Which get fatter when he speaks.

I can hear the crunching when he eats
I hear the stomping from his feet.

Aaron Ben Barber (9)
St Anne's RC Primary School, Birkenhead

If Only The World Had Better People

At the airport
Preparing for a flight
Excited about a holiday
Hard deserved
Looking for final
Holiday supplies
If only
The world had better people.

The plane's been hijacked
And we're in the sky
Defenceless
Why oh why?
Will we survive
Or will we die?
If only
The world had better people.

The plane's coming in
Causing a shroud
Of smoke and dust
We'd better get out
Will I survive
Or will I die?
If only
The world had better people.

Looking on the news
The Twin Towers are on fire
My family's there
Please not them
Will they survive
Or will they die?
If only
The world had better people.

Why our community
Why oh why?
What next?
It's not fair
We don't deserve it
Nobody does
If only

The world had better people.

Looking on the news
The Twin Towers are on fire
I must do my duty
And save lives
Will I survive
Or will I die?
If only the world had better people.

America as a whole
In despair
Determined
To stay together
And not let it
Happen ever again
If only
The world had better people.

The big attack
Is never far from minds
Causing many deaths
And sorrow
Now on the tenth anniversary
We look back
If only
The world had better people.

Ryan O'Neill (11)
St Bride's Primary School, Cambuslang

Gone But Never Forgotten

The day that death stalked America
How do I get out?
How do I help others?
Heroes emerge from the burning building,
Courageous emergency workers.
Seeds of hope for some,
Gone but not forgotten.

The day that death stalked America,
Anxiety for those who await,
Contacts not picking up,
Panic and hope flood family homes,
Enduring bonds of friendship,
Dead or alive
Gone but not forgotten.

The day that death stalked America
All affected by this terrible tragedy,
Devastation all over the world,
Tears flooded family homes,
Transportation grounded to a halt
Strong bonds of kinship
Gone but not forgotten.

The day that death stalked America
Jesus was the scene of 9/11
As the firemen climbed the staircases of the Twin Towers;
It was their hill of Calvary,
Out of the rubble of destruction,

Gone but not forgotten
The day that death stalked America
Deathly choice to jump or await your fate
Heroes emerge,
A nation of silence,
The vision of Hell!
Seeds of hope, dead or alive
Gone but not forgotten.

The day that death stalked America
A cocktail of violence
Billowing smoke and dust
A clean-up of death's destruction

The scale of horror
God bless them all
Gone but not forgotten

The day that death stalked America
A world full of broken hearts
A nation fell silent
At the scenes of a terrifying attack,
The sacrifices of so many lives from so many countries
It only . . .

Aidan Allan (11)
St Bride's Primary School, Cambuslang

The Destruction Of A Way Of Life

The lives lost on September 11th 2001
If only it hadn't happened, their lives would not be gone,
The sorrow of what happened made people feel ill,
People upset, what happened? Why? The day the world stood still,
The people in the buildings, first thought to mind is death.
How to escape, how are my family, what will happen next?
The chaos it caused,
The lives that were lost,
Are gone but not forgotten.

The family and friends of each of the victims grieve to this day,
They're filled with their deepest love, they are filled with fury,
Are they alive or are they dead? Is this the end for them?
They miss them, they love them, they need a hug, they were so hopeful at the time,
They tried to contact them in every way, because they loved them,
But all they did was to see if they were okay and then go back to their den.
Their destiny, their fate,
We could not debate,
They're gone but not forgotten.

The community listened to announcements, on radio and TV,
They were filled with love and sorrow, was their love too strong to be?
Silence engulfed the surrounding area, nothing seemed to be right,
They were all affected, every single one, if only there wasn't that flight,
The grieving has never stopped, never at all,
The tears, the wails, the crying, it was a massive fall,
The nation fell silent,
It was sudden and violent,
They're gone but not forgotten,

Modern day Calvary of the firemen and other services too,
Doctors and nurses all worked very hard, what happened?
Why? Who?
343 firemen were killed trying to save the others,
It could have been their family, their sisters, fathers, mothers,
Paramedics were zooming in ambulances to see who was okay,
A clear blue September sky: the darkest of all days,
Strong bonds of kinship,
A kiss on the lips,
They're gone but not forgotten.

Deafening silence on the aftermath, grief like a tidal wave,

Our countries unite in grief and loss, around the dreadful grave,
Stories of courage, where heroes emerge, the seeds of hope are planted,
Their love is not forgotten, as their names are ranted,
The Towers are gone, Hell visited that day,
10 years on we still grieve, it's not a sunshine ray,
A vision of Hell,
The choices that fell,
They are gone but definitely not forgotten.

Hannah MacArthur (10)
St Bride's Primary School, Cambuslang

The Day The World Stood Still

A clear blue September sky
New York City rushing around
World Trade Center busy
Then late in the afternoon
The north tower comes
Crashing down
Smoke and dust
Billowing down on New York City
The day the world stood still

29 minutes later the south tower comes down
More dust and smoke comes down on New York City
People start to run
Scared to death
Some people start to jump
And some people start to run
Newsflash appears on screens worldwide
Families watching husbands, friends, wives and kids see
The day the world stood still

New York City all affected
Devastated too
What will happen next?
Where will it happen next?
Radios turned on, world listening in
Phones are ringing but no answer
Listening for announcements on the TV, radios and phones
Extreme danger haunts New York City
The day the world stood still

Firemen 343 of them died
Losing their lives to save others
Doctors rushed off their feet
Surgeries open, surgeons busy treating patients
Horrific burns, bad cuts and
Life threatening injuries
The scenes were horrific
People with one arm, maybe one leg
The day the world stood still

Families grieved with the loss of their loved ones
One nation united to remember all those who died
They are determined

Determined to get the family back
Back together as one
Sad to know that their family will be left
Knowing that there is a part in their lives missing
But they know that they will still be looking down
The day the world finally stood still.

Erin Welsh (10)
St Bride's Primary School, Cambuslang

The Day The World Fell Silent

Some victims run with shock
But some don't even move
Some victims think of death
But others no time
Some victims think out the window
But some don't even dare
Some victims think of stairs
But jam-packed with others there
A nation fell silent

Families text and no reply
Families call, no answer, why?
Friends text and no reply
Friends call, no answer, why?
Families and friends hope and wait
But can't predict friends or loved ones' fate, only God can
Friends and families think why?
A nation fell silent.

Communities watch on television
Communities think, *oh why?*
Communities on radios
Thinking what or where next?
Communities filled with anger
Communities filled with no hope
Just with smirking smoke
Communities also think *who?*
A nation fell silent.

Rescue services running scared
Rescue services sick
Rescue services lost lives
To save others at will
Some rescuers lose arms
Some rescuers lose legs
A nation fell silent.

American citizens shocked
American citizens rushed
American citizens ran
Away from smoke and dust
Americans still can't believe
What happened on that day

The 9/11 disaster will never fade away
American citizens crushed
A nation and the world
Fell silent with a vision of Hell.

Brian McLean (11)
St Bride's Primary School, Cambuslang

Gone But Not Forgotten

Never forgetting the victims
Their suffering screams
Their thought of survival
Frozen with shock as they breathe their last
The haunting smoke that swamps their lungs
Their souls will never truly die
They will never crush our spirits

Never forgetting their friends and families
All they can do is plant seeds of hope
Worry fills their racing hearts
Relationships and friendships shattered
They see a scene of hell before their tear-filled eyes
They wait silently
They will never crush our spirits

Never forgetting the community
They are hurt
Fear and emotion flooding homes
What next?
Death is watching their every move
A layer of profound grief
They will never crush our spirits

Never forgetting the rescue services
The firemen rush past like lightning
The stairs haunted their minds
It was their hill of Calvary
Nurses and surgeons
More patients than stars in the heavens
They will never crush our spirits

Never forgetting the aftermath
United in grief . . .
And in sorrow . . .
Heartbroken at the sight
Determined for justice
Hungry for glory
They will never crush our spirits

Never forgetting 10 years later
We still remember the sorrow
All are still affected

And still mourn the dead
We all stand united
A nation, a world in tears
They will never crush our spirits.

Eve Kelly (11)
St Bride's Primary School, Cambuslang

89

On The Day Of Death

A day to remember, a day of death,
Planes flew into the Twin Towers, on the day of death.
Victims left screaming for life, on the day of death.
Passengers shocked, bewildered on the day of death.
Who will survive? Who will be unlucky? We'll all find out, on the day of death.
Why did they do it? Nobody knows, but we all know it happened on the day of death.

Mums, dads, brothers, sisters praying relatives are OK on the day of death.
Are they dead? They don't know, but it all happened on the day of death.
Friendships crushed, marriages ruined, it all happened on the day of death.
Hearts pounding as fast as a cheetah chasing after its prey, it all happened on the day of death.
Worried, scared, terrified, shocked, all the feelings on the day of death,
Trying to contact, probably can't, panic all over on the day of death.

The community watching as Hell unveiled before them,
That's what happened on the day of death.
Why did it happen? What happens next? We'll all find out on the day of death.
Run from the smoke, from this terrible tragedy, run away on this day of death.
Were the planes hijacked? Was it an accident? We'll all find out on the day of death.
Everyone screaming, everyone shocked, that's what happened on the day of death.
The community fell silent when the planes hit the Towers
That's what happened on the day of death.

Firemen came, some never returned on the day of death.
343 firemen died but all a heroes death, they all died on the day of death.
Doctors, nurses and surgeons too, they all helped on the day of death.
Everyone played a part, on the day of death.
Doctors and nurses tried their best, to save the victims of the day of death.
Firemen were as determined to save the victims as a dog trying to catch its tail,
They were determined on the day of death.

The Americans united after the tragedy occurred, that happened on the day of death.
They shared a common bond of grief and loss, they shared that bond on the day of death.
A united nation is what is left, what was left of the day of death.
The destruction of a way of life, a nation, a world in tears, the tears of the day of death.
Heroes have emerged from the day of death.
Gone but not forgotten, all this happened on the day of death.

Joseph Cassidy (11)
St Bride's Primary School, Cambuslang

The Day America Fell Silent

The day America fell silent
The people of the Twin Towers terrified with fear
Hell visited the World Trade Centre that day
Deathly choice to jump or wait your fate
The planes smashed into the Twin Towers like a man smashes glass
Suffering breaks our world like a tree struck by lightning
The day that death stalked America
Gone but not forgotten

The day America stood still
Family try to contact but get no answer
Friends anxious about friends who are in the Towers
Family worry about relatives
Friends and family pleading for their sake
Why did someone fly the planes into the towers?
Family contact to say final farewell
Gone but not forgotten

The most tragic community wound
The community of New York devastated with the disaster
What or where next nobody knows
Anger strikes America like lightning strikes a tree
America wondered who did it but nobody knew
The world wonders why it happened but it is still unknown
All devastated by the mass of destruction
Gone but not forgotten

The day the world stood still
The firefighters climbed the stairs to save others
343 firefighters died as heroes
Fire encompassed the inhabitants
Firefighters fought the flames
Doctors and nurses fought to save as many lives as possible
Surgeons also fought to save lives
Gone but not forgotten

Deafening silence in the aftermath
Smoke billowed from the Twin Towers
Grief is like a tidal wave

Untied in grief and courage
America determined to build new Twin Towers
Our country unites
Gone but not forgotten.

Dean Holden
St Bride's Primary School, Cambuslang

93

We'll Never Forget The Souls Of 9/11

We'll never forget the souls of 9/11
How can we escape?
The panic is out of control
Why?
All the *chaos*
Screaming
Shouting
Are we near death?

We'll never forget the souls of 9/11
Tears flood
Worry shrieks
Hope is awaiting
Why?
Families scared
Friends praying
Mercy calling!

We'll never forget the souls of 9/11
Devastation is here
Why would anyone do such a thing?
Who started 9/11?
The Earth stopped
Watching
Listening
What will happen next?

We'll never forget the souls of 9/11
Heroes
343 firemen lost their lives
Sacrificing for others
Petrified
Think
Doctors
Nurses!

We'll never forget the souls of 9/11
Determination at the core
Who?
Why?
You will never know
Petrified
Grief has appeared
Make sure It will never happen again!

Rebekah Bain
St Bride's Primary School, Cambuslang

Who And Why?

The day the world stood still
A day of loss and grief
The panic
The chaos
Wondering if death is near
How to escape?
Drowning in panic
Who and why?

Awaiting families was devastated
When images of destruction flashed
Screens world wide
Wondering, dead or alive
Wondering, thinking, hoping
Worrying
Praying and pleading
They will be alright
Who and why?

The community scarred for life
Wondering where next
Silence engulfed the surrounding areas
On the day, that made the world stand still
Devastation filled the air
All listening to the radio
Trying to believe it
Who and why?

Firefighters trying to rescue people
Doctors and nurses trying to save people
Wondering should they go in and rescue people
343 firefighters killed
280 badly burned
Gone but not forgotten
Courageous emergency workers
Who and why?

America citizens devastated
A nation, a world in tears
United in grief and loss
United in courage
Determined to find out who did it
United together
But who and why?

Charlotte Smith
St Bride's Primary School, Cambuslang

Who And Why?

The flames engulf the room
Like the gates of Hell have opened before your feet
Asking yourself to either jump or await your fate
How do you escape?
Even although the fire rages
You are frozen by fear
You think to yourself . . .
Who and why?

Your family tried to contact you
They plead to God you're alive
Inexplicable fear strikes their bodies
Like a vulture swooping in for a dive
What do they do?
They anxiously await
They think to themselves
Who and why?

The community watch the horror unfold
They have a devastated look on their faces
They wonder where next?
People watch in horror to see if their loved ones are alright
They hope others are okay
Anger fills their body
They think to themselves
Who and why?

The firemen rush out to the scene
They see the commotion
They rush up the stairs
To see if there is anyone there
And lose their lives doing so
But hope is not lost . . .
The firemen think to themselves
Who and why?

The American citizens think *is all hope gone?*
Has hope stood up and walked out the door?
No, they are determined to continue living their lives
Life goes on!
They are still united as a country
But that moment will never fade
They think to themselves . . .
Who and why?

Stephen Hunt (11)
St Bride's Primary School, Cambuslang

But Why?

The sacrifices of so many lives,
The day death stalked America,
When not just a building was destroyed
But a nation too,
Gone but not forgotten,
They live on in people's hearts,
Terrified as they ran to safety,
Echoes of their screams and cries for help,
But why?

Families await . . . Hope
Images of destruction flashed screens worldwide
The destruction of a way of life,
Families receive news and well up as they hear,
People as crushed as Twin Towers,
But why?

Communities pay tribute,
All as devastated as the other,
Cries like the most tragic community wound,
They share their sorrows,
Silence deafens the nations,
United in grief and loss,
United in courage,
But why?

Rescue services come to save,
343 die on their way,
Surgeons, firefighters lose their lives,
To let others see another day,
Assigned to jobs they go in,
But they might not come back out,
Heroes die,
But why?

Citizens united,
And determined to rise up from the past,
Yet still down,
They continue their lives,
This will be there forever,
But why?

Lukhvir Kumar (11)
St Bride's Primary School, Cambuslang

The Day The World Stood Still

A clear blue September sky: the darkest of days
3,000 lives lost.
The smoke covered the sky.
People crying everywhere you look,
So many deaths from so many countries,
Everywhere covered in dust like the world had never cleaned.
People gone but not forgotten.

Friends lost, families lost.
Friendships crushed like broken bones.
Families watching TV crying, hoping that their family member is spared.
Friends trying to call their friends,
Phone lines blocked with all the calls.
Families and friends furious at what they have seen.
The day a nation fell silent.

New York fell silent like nobody was on the world.
The community hid in their homes.
The community watched as people jumped to their deaths.
The thud when they landed.
The day that death stalked New York.
The sirens of fire engines and ambulances ringing in your ears,
Bodies laid out in the streets.

Firemen rushing in and out of the towers.
Firemen coming out with bodies
Firemen sacrificing their lives to save others.
Ambulances coming in and going out.
343 firemen who sacrificed that day.
Firemen coming out covered in dirt,
If only it hadn't happened.

The aftermath never forgotten.
The country unites.
America in grief like a little baby crying.
America determined to build them again.
America rise out of the rubble of fear.
Heroes emerge.
The day America will never forget.
The day the world stood still.

Jack Stewart
St Bride's Primary School, Cambuslang

The Day That Changed The World

If only they knew how to escape
If there weren't as many people losing their lives
Why they did it
The panic flooded America
They will never crush our spirits
They're gone but not forgotten

Are they alive or dead?
The hope around America
The destruction of a way of life
Are mums and dads still alive?
Sons and daughters may have lost their lives
Gone but not forgotten

The community was all affected
A nation, a world of tears
The most tragic community wound
In extreme danger
They will never crush our spirits
Gone but not forgotten

The sacrifice of so many lives from so many countries
Doctors and nurses tend the badly injured
The 343 firemen who lost their lives through saving others
A nation that fell silent
Jesus was there that day
Gone but not forgotten

The chaos all over America
A scale of horror
A vision of Hell!

Flowers, signed condolence books
The day the world stood still
Hell visited the Twin Towers that day
Heroes emerge
They will never crush our spirits
Gone but not forgotten.

James Duffy (11)
St Bride's Primary School, Cambuslang

103

The Day The World Stood Still

The day the world stood still
The billowing smoke and dust
A layer of anxiety
The panic on the plane
The questions being asked, 'Why? Why? Why?'
Gone but not forgotten.

The day the world fell silent
Families pleading, worried and anxious
If only the people were somewhere else
Alive or dead? Alive or dead? The scale of the horror
The Twin Towers fell like the tower in Jenga
Gone but not forgotten.

The day the world broke into tears
Awaiting the call from their beloved ones
The most tragic community wounds
A cocktail of violence
The traffic ground to a halt
Gone but not forgotten.

The day the world was bewildered
Grief like a tidal wave
Deafening silence in the aftermath
United grief and loss
Seed of hope spread everywhere
Gone but not forgotten.

The day that death stalked America
The heroes emerge
The sacrifice of so many lives from so many countries
Out of the rubble of destruction
Courageous emergency workers
Gone but not forgotten.

Luke McGunnigle
St Bride's Primary School, Cambuslang

104

If Only . . .

If only we could rewind back 10 years
If only we could be stopped
If only we could live again
If only the dark could change to light
If only I could get out
But Jesus was there that day

Why them?
Are they alive or dead?
We may never know . . .
How can I contact them?
Who did this terrible trade?
But Jesus was there that day

A shroud of smoke and dust
A layer of profound grief
A crush of simple sorrow
A sound of deep fear
Only a glimpse of hope
But Jesus was there that day

Firefighters awaiting life or death
Climbing up the stairs of the smoky towers
Desperately climbing out of the rubble of destruction
For some it was their hill of Calvary
For others a hint of hope
But Jesus was there that day

A national disaster
The sacrifice of so many lives from so many countries
A nation, a world of tears
United in grief and loss
United in courage
But Jesus was there that day.

Louise Kelly
St Bride's Primary School, Cambuslang

Glory For England

The stand was filling up rapidly,
I couldn't wait.
I saw the players running onto the pitch
Moore, Hurst, Peters,
It was a great day for a match
Especially for a World Cup Final.
The crowd went silent . . .
The match had started.
England scored first, with a great goal from Geoff Hurst,
The crowd went wild, screaming and shouting.
The match went on to be 2-2.
Geoff Hurst and Martin Peters had scored one each.
Now they were crouching beside manager Alf Ramsey
Getting ready for extra time.
As the whistle blew for extra time,
England stormed forward and banged in another goal.
As the end of the match grew nearer
I got really nervous.
It was the last minute
'Some of the crowd were on the pitch,' said the commentator
'They think it's all over,'
Suddenly Hurst pinged in his hat trick.
'It is now.'
The whistle blew,
It was all over.
I saw the men coming up the stairs.
Moore with a big smile on his face.
Finally they made it up.
The crowd screamed.
It was done.

Billy Dewhurst (10)
St Clare's Catholic Primary School, Preston

This Is It

This is it.
At the Groote Schuur Hospital.
There are surgeons and doctors rushing around.
My gloves are covered in blood.
The Cardiac Bypass Machine is beeping.
My hands are shaking.
My heart is thumping.
I am about to make history.
Professor Wagensteen is watching closely.
I slowly lift out the heart.
Everybody stops.
Time slows.
The machine has stopped.
A surgeon hands me Mr Darval's heart.
I am sweating as I lower it into Mr Wahskansky's body.
Suddenly the heart slips.
I just manage to hold onto it.
There is a deathly silence.
Then . . .
I put it in.
Will he live?
Will he die?
No one knows.
Beep . . .
Beep . . .
Beep . . .
The machine comes to life.
Then everyone cheers and claps.
'I've done it,
I've made history.'

Joshua Fowler (10)
St Clare's Catholic Primary School, Preston

107

The Start Of A Legacy

The presidential limo, midnight blue,
American flags fluttering in the wind,
came round the corner of Dealey Plaza.
The crowd cheered,
hoping to get a glimpse of their President,
John F Kennedy.
Kennedy waved back, smiling.
Jackie Kennedy sat next to him.
The Governor of Texas, John Connolly,
sat in front of him.
His motorcade snaked behind him.
Kennedy leaned out to get a better look at the crowds . . .

Bang! Kennedy slumped forward.
Jackie wondered what had happened.
The Governor turned round.
Bang! The president jerked backwards.
The Governor cried out.
Jackie was screaming.
She tried to get away.
Bang! An FBI agent jumped onto the back bumper.
The limo sped away to the nearest hospital.
Jackie was still screaming . . .

President Kennedy was pronounced dead at 1pm,
About 25 minutes later.
John Fitzgerald Kennedy.
One man.
One assassin.
The start of a legacy.

Aaron Leigh (10)
St Clare's Catholic Primary School, Preston

Unexpected Death

On the 22nd of November happened history's greatest tragedy,

This was the date of the assassination of President Kennedy.

Thousands gathered in the crowd,
Shouting and yelling out aloud,

To catch a glimpse of JFK
The 35th president of the USA

Shots rang out from near and far,
Within seconds, off sped the car.

News broke that the president was dead,
With a bullet straight to the head.

Rumours were around who shot the gun
One thing's for sure, the damage was done.

Was it because he wanted to end the Vietnam War?
Is that why he was shot from the Book Depository store?

All the citizens wept in the great US of A, though time has moved on and it will never forget its darkest day.

So was it Oswald or the work of a gang?
Because on that day the world heard its biggest . . . Bang!

George Brown (11)
St Clare's Catholic Primary School, Preston

Hey Doctor December 3rd 1967

'Hey doctor, what happens if we can't re-attach his heart?
Hey doctor, what happens is his blood stops circulating?
Hey doctor, what happens if he runs out of oxygen?
Hey doctor, what happens if he wakes up?
Hey doctor, what happens if his new heart doesn't work?
Hey doctor, what happens if he loses too much blood?
Hey doctor, what happens if a part of his heart falls off?
Hey doctor, what happens if . . .'

'Be quiet!'

Matthew Adams (10)
St Clare's Catholic Primary School, Preston

A Giant Leap For Mankind

Millions of people watching this very moment
Lowering his left foot, right foot
'That's one small step for man,
One giant leap for mankind.'
The moon is 4-5 billion years old,
It feels like powdered charcoal.
As he skips across the surface,
His heavy moon boots hold him down.
The craters are feet deep.
Shaped like a satellite dish.
He sees wonderful patterns
As he drives in the Lunar Rover
He plays golf when he is there,
He bids farewell after two and a half hours.
When he gets back in the rocket,
It is low on fuel.
I bet he is thinking
We have won the race in the Soviet Union
After a while he heads back to Earth
Saying goodbye to the mystical moon.

Megan Maguire-Baxter (10)
St Clare's Catholic Primary School, Preston

Bang! Bang!

It was a sunny day
He walked on the balcony,
The assassin's heart was pounding,
He was looking out of the balcony
Suddenly there was a *bang! Bang!*
He was shot twice and killed at the Lorraine Motel!
It was the end for Martin Luther King Junior.
The assassin felt bad
The gun felt bad.
Martin Luther King Junior
Was 38 and had a heart like an old man.

Victoria Law
St Clare's Catholic Primary School, Preston

1966 Was Where It All Started

1966 was where it all started
A s the big cup game began,
B ritain was nervous but excited.
C aptain Bobby Moore was running towards the goal post,
D etermined Hurst was to score!
E veryone was cheering and shouting,
F or this was it, the time had come . . .
G oal! Germany were going down!
H urst scored 3, Peters 1!
I t was nearly over,
J ust as Germany were going down they scored!
K illing England's excitement, 'Oh no!'
L ittle? No *big* trophy was to spare!
M artin was scared, but really excited,
N ow seconds left, 'Come on!'
'O h no!' Game was over but yes we'd done it!
P roud England won the World Cup 4-2!
Q ueen presented the big gold trophy.
R amsey was over the moon!

Heather Fletcher (10)
St Clare's Catholic Primary School, Preston

He Had A Dream

In 1964, Martin Luther King Junior won the Nobel Peace Prize

He led mass protests against discriminatory practices
Assassinated on 4th April 1968 during a visit to Memphis, Tennessee
Voting rights act outlawing the discriminatory practices
Equality for all would become a reality in America

Arrested and jailed for his part in the protests

Direct action based on the methods of Gandhi
Released, then participated in the enormous civil rights march in Washington
Evening at the Lorrain Hotel he was shot in the neck whilst standing on the
     balcony
A campaign to register blacks to vote
Message of peaceful protests,

Lucy (10)
St Clare's Catholic Primary School, Preston

Who Would Do Such A Thing?

'What a day, eh?'
'Yeah, oh here he comes.'
'Wow this ama-.'
Bang!
'What was that?'
'The president, he's, he's be-.'
Bang, bang!
'Get to the 5th floor at the Texas Book Depository!'
'OK.'
'OK, what happened?'
'The president was shot from this floor.'
'How do you know?'
'It was the only window what was open in this building.'
'What are all these boxes for?'
'I don't know, kick them down, I've got my gun.'
'What's that?'
'A bucket of fried chicken and . . . A Carcano rifle!'
'Don't worry I've already reported it.'

Jack Thomas (10)
St Clare's Catholic Primary School, Preston

The Sound Of . . .

John F Kennedy was assassinated on the 22nd of November 1963.
'This morning JFK is coming to Dallas,'
Said the radio reports around Texas,
Dealey Plaza was full of people.
JFK was waving and was very pleased to see all the people.
The sound of screaming and shouting woke up Dallas.
'Are you still OK John?' said Jackie at the top of her voice.
Jackie heard the sound of
Bang!
Bang!
Bang! ring out.
That put Dallas back to sleep in shock and Kennedy was a part of the sleep.
35 minutes later Kennedy would not wake up . . .

Michaela Halsey (10)
St Clare's Catholic Primary School, Preston

Gone Was The President

President Kennedy
Born on the 29th of May 1917.
President of America
When he was 42.
The youngest
President at that time.
He was in Texas in his open top car
Driving to Dallas.
The streets were
Lined like a slithering snake and they
Drove round the bend on Dealey Plaza.
Bang! Bang! Bang!
Kennedy was shot.
People screaming, people shouting,
Children crying and people running.
The car sped off with Kennedy and his wife.
The governor of Texas was in the car and he was shot too.
Kennedy had gone.

Lucas (11)
St Clare's Catholic Primary School, Preston

Winners!

England wins the World Cup for the first time in 36 years.
Against West Germany,
93,000 spectators including the Queen
And Prince Philip watched it.
Geoff Hurst levelled the score with a header
From Bobby Moore's free kick.
Wembley Stadium was full and the
Spectators covered the whole of London.
Geoff Hurst scored a hat-trick,
With that England won 4-2 and became
The champions for the first time.
'Hooray!'
'I'm so happy, it's the first time in thirty six years.'

Jordan McGrath (10)
St Clare's Catholic Primary School, Preston

Three Bullets And . . . Dead!

On the 22nd of November 1963.
The president JFK visits Texas.
He comes past the bend in Dealey Plaza,
I am in the crowd with my mate
Zapruder.
Everybody is happy, cheering and shouting.
It is a really nice day.
Bang!
Bang!
Bang!
The President has been shot with a gun,
One of the USA's biggest horrors has begun.
The President fell to the car floor covered in blood,
Where I stood there was some mud.
He has been shot in the head,
Then rushed to a hospital bed.
The day was over, it had been horrible.

Tom Lutan (10)
St Clare's Catholic Primary School, Preston

1960s What's With The LEGO?

In 1960 Britain found LEGO,
Children playing with towers of yellow.
Mum's come in shouting,
Finding LEGO on their outing.

'Ole Kirk Christainsen,' they say,
'That's all the children play.'
'Mum, the red brick is coming soon,'
'Me and Jack will make a balloon!'

'Det beste er ikke for godt', is the LEGO motto,
Which means, 'only the best is good enough',
First came yellow, red then blue,
And all the others followed too.

Emma O'Reilly (10)
St Clare's Catholic Primary School, Preston

The Surgery Of Fright

The heart is a great muscle,
Keeping blood pumping through the body.
One man performing the most dangerous surgery ever,
A heart transplant.
His name is Doctor Barnard and
Thoughts were rushing through his head.
The nurse was coming in . . . and . . . out with tools.
Stress,
Pain,
Worry
He could see it in the patient's eyes,
It then changed.
The worry now over,
The surgery a success.
He was relieved he did it and
The nurse had a huge grin on her face of joy.
Everything was over.

Matthew Halucha (10)
St Clare's Catholic Primary School, Preston

Goodbye Kennedy

John Fitzgerald Kennedy.
Lee Harvey Oswald shot you
Down! Down!
Deeper and *down!*
When you visited Dallas, Texas Town.
Are you angry with Lee Harvey Oswald?
In New York
They named an airport after you
It still stands today.

Adam Stewart (10)
St Clare's Catholic Primary School, Preston

Wembley Is Alive

England won in 1966 30th July
England's captain Bobby Moore
England's manager Alf Ramsey
England won at Wembley
England scored some cracking goals
England played West Germany
England won 4-2
England won the cup for the first time
England have they won it for the last . . . time?

Bobby Moore walks over to me, he picks me up and . . .
The Queen is smiling,
The crowd is screaming,
3-2-1-
Yeah!
England have won the cup
Alf Ramsey is as jolly as a young boy.

James Greenwood (10)
St Clare's Catholic Primary School, Preston

JFK

On the 22nd of November 1963,
Thousands gathered in the streets of Dallas,
To get a glimpse of JFK
The 35th president of the USA
He was going to the town hall,
To give a speech.
He was in the middle of the street
In his dark blue navy limo,
Then suddenly, *bang! Bang! Bang!*
There was a bullet through his neck,
Through his head, and a bullet
Went through Governor Connolly.
Was it Oswald or was he in a gang?
Now the limo is off in a rush to the hospital.
Now, he lies on a hospital bed.
Now everyone knows he is dead.

P J Allen (11)
St Clare's Catholic Primary School, Preston

Glory For England

Goal! Geoff Hurst had scored the opening goal.
I felt so happy.

Goal! West Germany had got an equaliser.
I felt so sad.
It was like the defence had let the keeper down.

Goal! Martin Peters had got the lead.
I felt like we were back on top of the world.

Goal! West Germany had got an equaliser again.
I felt a little down but we could get a goal back.

Goal! Geoff Hurst had got a second goal.
We're back in!

Goal! In the final dying moments Geoff Hurst had got a hat-trick.
It was the moment of my life, getting a hat-trick in a
World Cup Final.

Luke Ellis (11)
St Clare's Catholic Primary School, Preston

The Apprentice House

A fter work in the Apprentice House, stale bread to eat
P rayers were said for they got hurt in the mill, not sweet!
P lease help me I'm in the Apprentice School.
R eading cures from the list is Mr Shawcross
E very day someone got punished with a whip
N ow even worse he uses the tip!
T oday I was one of many with a sore lip,
I got the leeches on it, they looked eew when they did a flip!
C an Mr Shawcross be mean?
E veryone can, but Mr S gives you the dumbbells

H e gives the whip if words spelt wrong
O ut there I'd rather be
U nder here it isn't just me
S ome others, like 60 of us!
E veryone never makes a fuss!

Charlotte Croughan (10)
St George's CE Primary School, Westhoughton

You Wouldn't Want To Be A Vile Victorian

This is where my story begins
Sitting here cold and thin
Quiet as a mouse I sit down
First day at school not going well
Had the cane it killed like hell

Lunch time hooray it's finally come
Maybe I could run away
Too late, they've locked the gate
Don't know what to do Sir
Go away and maybe you will find someone to play with boy
Then the whistle blew
Back to class I flew
For the afternoon lessons

Registers done now it's PE
It can't be so bad
I was wrong, Sir is tough
People going pant, pant, pant touching their toes
I'm tired out, want to stop
But I must carry on so I don't get lashed

Back inside is it finally home time?
No just drawing parts of machines
It's so tricky and my drawing's black
You see I spilt ink and it's gone on the front and back!

Ring, ring, ring
It's home time (finally)
Mother's here to pick me up
Hooray.

Scarlet Allardice (9)
St George's CE Primary School, Westhoughton

Teachers

Teachers call
Mothers bawl,

Children pale white
Parents in a fight,

Apprentices trek
While my eyes wreck,

I rob a ship
And my friend gets the whip,

Fathers weep
Up the steep,

Brothers wept
Sisters kept,

Round the door
The kids want more,

Heads complain
I'm in pain,

Babies wail
The weather's hail,

Uncles row
But how?

Rianna Green (9)
St George's CE Primary School, Westhoughton

Vile Victorians

I hear the mills running round really loud and it hurts my ears.
I can smell old rusty metal in the mills and kids working really hard.
I see water dripping off an old pipe in the classroom.
I touched a white board and it glowed.
I can see kids playing and writing.
I can hear children moaning and groaning.

Jack Barton (9)
St George's CE Primary School, Westhoughton

Vile Victorians

V ile Victorians, so mean and cruel!
I llness so horrid you feel sick
C lanking machines you can't fall asleep
T errible leeches massive and huge
O ff bread to eat all day
R ushing children trying not to be late
I n the corner children wearing dunce's hat
A pprentice house is our home forever
N ow I know a lot more, I can read and write
S unday church again, walking there and back

A pprentice house has provided a lot
R eading books and writing
E nd of day all go to bed for the next day

C ruel as a witch flying
R ushing to school again
U ncle Joe gone back to work
E ating porridge again and again
L ate nights are not good for work.

Melikie Atilgan (9)
St George's CE Primary School, Westhoughton

Being A Kid In Victorian Times

If you were a kid you would work in a mill
I would sign with a quill
I would see lots of machines
It was so loud and clanking, banging and busy
If you would want to speak you would use sign language
it was that loud.
After a hard day at work you would go to school
Saying do not act like a fool.
I can hear silence.
Then it is potato for dinner.
Then it's bed time.
I look in the clouds and it goes dimmer and dimmer.

Adam Frankland (9)
St George's CE Primary School, Westhoughton

The Mill

If I worked in a mill I would write with a quill and
I'd wait for my weekly wages.
If I wanted more food I'd be classed rude and
No one will want to talk to me.

I'd be bored all day with nothing to say and
I wouldn't get any money for pay.
Cleaning machines, risking my life just for two shillings.

My family need money so they left me here
And I wasn't allowed to leave.
After a long works day, without any pay,
All the children would want to run away.

After work we go back up the hill away from the mill
To get food from the boss.
He'd teach us lessons, not giving us blessings
And gives us medicine that makes us vomit.
After a lovely tea that he made for me it's time to go to bed.
I pull up the blanket to go to sleep, it's so quiet it makes me weep!

Max Kenny (10)
St George's CE Primary School, Westhoughton

The Cane

The day I had the cane I was in a lot of pain
Here's how it went, I was in the yard at school
I didn't like school so I ran away.

Outside it was misty I couldn't see a thing
But then I heard a sound.
I had heard it before.

Then I got it, it was the headmaster's shoes
Then he pulled me by the ear.
He then took me in a room I had never been in.
Then he whipped me 10 times on the legs and 4 times on the back
I will never run away again.

Alisha Mather (10)
St George's CE Primary School, Westhoughton

121

The Mill

I could see the cold dusty mill,
The cotton smell itched my nose,
This figure out of nowhere grabbed me,
So tightly I could feel my arm burning like a raging fire.

He said to me I'll be working in this mill
I could hear the machine clanking and yelling
It nearly deafened me,
This figure kept pulling and pulling me
Then this figure took me to the mill,
And he said to me, 'You will be working in this mill chap,'
Now we were in the light I could see this figure now,
He was a normal sized man, he had ginger hair,
Just like mine,
So I had to ask, 'Sir, do you know anyone of the name
Charles Burnly?'
'Yes, he's my son, I haven't seen him since he was a baby.'
'Well Sir, I am Charles Burnley Sir, your son!'

Charlotte Burchill (10)
St George's CE Primary School, Westhoughton

Victorians

V icious vile Victorians
I gnorant Victorians
C ruel Victorians
T errible Victorians
O riginal Victorians
R uling Victorians
I magine being a Victorian child
A ngry Victorians
N aughty Victorians
S o mean Victorians.

Louie (10)
St George's CE Primary School, Westhoughton

Victorian Scare

The vile Victorians have a scare
No wonder they're mean, there's some over there
They're up and they're down, they work in the mill
They hardly have time to call me Will.
I can hear, I can see
It's not just me.

On the other hand school is strict
With a cane and a whip.
I really don't want the dunce's hat
I want to see a black cat.

If I was small that would be good
I've not even got a best bud.

This poem is called Victorian scare
Come on man, it's not fair!

Thomas Higham (9)
St George's CE Primary School, Westhoughton

The Working Victorians

In the work house the children were the poorest of the poor,
They had a handful of porridge for breakfast but they always wanted more.

In the mill they had to earn their keep,
Although it never helped when they gave a little weep.

In the mill the engineers got twenty two shillings,
Even when they broke their teeth they couldn't be mended because they hadn't
yet invented fillings.

In the apprentice house they worked morning till night,
And if they couldn't afford shoes they got the occasional rat bite.

At school when they were breaking stones,
They usually never broke their bones.

Women could never read or write
So the clerks had to teach them but they never taught at night.

Sapphire Boydell (10)
St George's CE Primary School, Westhoughton

123

Victorians

V ictorian children worked all day
I n the apprentice house they learnt
C hildren cleaned noisy machines
T hey went to school and got a whip
O h and the machines were very noisy too
R ags they wore
I went to work at 6.30am
A llowed payments, but not very much
N ot much money
S mashing and screeching machines.

Sophie Fazal (9)
St George's CE Primary School, Westhoughton

Victorians

V ictorian houses were very small
I nk was what they put quills in
C urding machines were very noisy
T rains were popular in those days
O h no it is porridge today
R otten teeth Victorians had
I would not like to be a Victorian
A very noisy workhouse
N aughty children got the cane.

William Redman (9)
St George's CE Primary School, Westhoughton

124

Vicious Victorian School

As I looked through the broken door,
I could see boys, rich and poor.
Each one of them stood up in shock,
'Cause they have to answer against the clock.

One little boy was wearing the dunce hat,
And strangely one boy acted like a cat.
One a dog, one a pig,
And one that loved eating figs.

As a teacher just likes shouting,
And none of the classes enjoyed chanting.
He lost his rag when we were talking,
But we just thought he was plain boring.

A blackbird rattles on its cage,
When it fills with a mad rage.
He just sits there and stares at Pete,
If he doesn't get his daily treat.

Some boys have ink sinking into their skin,
They say it hurts as much as a pin.
It isn't as bad as having the cane,
And screaming out in lots of pain.

Alexander February (10)
St Joseph's RC Primary School, Washington

Terrible Victorian Street

I see a baker's bread buns fly through the air,
Lots of children begin to share.
Well dressed people wander around,
A pauper watched as a girl shows a pound.
A prosperous man wearing his dark red suit,
A shiny, black boot on each foot.

I can feel the warmth of the gravy running down my throat,
My last shilling spent on the pie I just bought.
The freezing cold cobbled stones,
Made my feet freeze to the bones.

Jennifer Louise Nuttall (10)
St Joseph's RC Primary School, Washington

The Old Street

What can you see?
The flickering light of the candle in the foggy darkness
The policeman who took the children to the workhouse
While they screamed, you're heartless.
The poor children can't afford school.
Never mind if they were cool.
The children in barefoot on the road
The children playing in the school yard with metal.

What can you hear?
The clip-clopping of horses' hooves on pebbled streets
The clatter of wooden wheels on the cobbled ground.
The chewing of the children who are lucky enough to eat.

What can you feel?
The soft breeze of the soft wind
The sadness of children in the workhouse
The soft fur of a mouse.

Heather Moss (10)
St Joseph's RC Primary School, Washington

The Victorian Streets

As I see a pickpocket facedly glee,
As they run to an unlucky victim.
They whipped out a sixpence it was so frightening,
It was as quick as zipping lightning.

As I hear weeping boys,
As they were scraping their wooden toys.
The policemen shouts at these two rugged boys,
As they steal these two boys toys.

Now I feel sad as I got beat like mad,
The crying orphans crunched up so bad they're crying because they've got no dad.
Now I feel so happy I created a house for the homeless who don't have a dad,
Who were crying like mad.

Jason Storey (10)
St Joseph's RC Primary School, Washington

The Dreaded Street

Pickpockets snatch the rich man's wallet.
They're gone as quick as a whip.
Chimney sweepers walk past me with their sweeps.
Their faces as black as a bat.
The drab and dust coming from them show they're sad
They saw me and said you better be glad.

Clip, clop, clip, clop, sounds the horse's hooves.
Crash, crash he's always going to lose.
'Come here you,' screamed the angry men.
'Hurry up, are you bringing down the hem!'

My bare feet dash in the cobbles.
I've got to keep running or I'm in trouble.
I'd rather sleep in the humble streets, shrivelled and cold.
I detest the workhouse, I don't want to be told.
I'm not going there, I'm safe in this box.
It's -10° now, it's getting colder and colder and colder . . .

Olivia Jayne Lynn (10)
St Joseph's RC Primary School, Washington

Street Scene

Horses getting whipped by the men in the golden carriages,
Barefooted children sweeping the dirty road,
A flame flickering inside a box lighting up the gloomy street,
A man lying on the floor who has been beat.

Clip clopping of horse's hooves on the cobbled path,
Rattling of the wooden clapper, a small boy is holding,
Shouts of policemen echoing down the street,
An old man sitting on a wooden seat.

Wet puddles soaking into my shoes,
Wind brushing against my hair,
Worries all around me,
Sweet strumming of a violin down the road,
A lady's hat getting sold.

Blythe Doyle (10)
St Joseph's RC Primary School, Washington

127

A Victorian Street

What can you see?
The horse's hooves clattered
When the man battered
All of the people rushing
And almost everyone pushing

What can you hear?
Children screaming
And they were loudly pleading
Children chanting
They were already panting

What can you feel?
The cold shiver
I want to quiver
The cobbles on my feet
It feels like heat.

Robert Carr (10)
St Joseph's RC Primary School, Washington

The Windy Street

What can you see?
A warm flickery flame in a tall street lamp,
There is fog everywhere and the floor is very damp.
Barefoot children wander the streets begging for food,
The chimney sweeps have black sooty faces after a lot of cramp.

What can you hear?
Horse's hooves clip-clopping in the cobble ground,
Down town, an angry policeman is shouting at homeless children.
Crying children in the crowded street,
In a cold river a little girl drowned.

What can you feel?
The cold wind in the dark alleyway,
I shiver off the shouting.
Sorry for the lonely children,
Dizzy after the women shouting, 'You need to pay!'

Ellie Jane Henderson (10)
St Joseph's RC Primary School, Washington

The Normalities Of A Victorian Street

Horses clip-clopped down the dirty street,
Broken hooves on their grimy, fat feet
Children playing in the gutter,
They imagined with a mutter.

Lights gleamed by one single candle
That made a gleaming door handle
A church bell ringing,
The choir singing.

Frustrated people waiting at the church door,
They were angry, they couldn't wait anymore
Pickpockets rustling through my pockets,
Stealing watches and ladies' lockets.

Zainib Qureshi (10)
St Joseph's RC Primary School, Washington

The Victorian Street

I see children running home from school.
The teachers were really cruel.
Drab clothes all around,
People sleeping on the ground.

I hear the clip clopping of horse's hooves
And a stomp of the shoes.
The clutter of the rush
Rustling coming from a bush.

I feel the wind over my face.
The scratching of my clothes of lace.
I get bumped by passersby,
Then I give out a really big sigh.

Megan Ann Webb (10)
St Joseph's RC Primary School, Washington

A Victorian Street

What can you see?
Pickpockets in a top hat man's pocket, wanting his money.
Flicking candles lighting the dim hallway.
Children picking their knees waiting to sneeze.

What can you hear?
Clip clopping of horses hooves on the floor.
Men shouting at them to make them go faster.
All shouted by the master.

What can you feel?
When horses get shouted at they sit on a mat.
But when a rat comes at them, they shout like a cat.
The men shout at them, so then it's time to say goodnight.

Emily Bruce (10)
St Joseph's RC Primary School, Washington

A Victorian Street

Roasted chestnuts for a penny
Maids selling milk for a pound
Under the flickering light
In the dead of night

Clippety claps of horse's hooves
Sobbing of children lost
Escaped work house children screaming yay
Till the end of day

The sadness of children sobbing
A lonely man down the road
Your feet will freeze all day long
Happiness of a man who just had his top hat sold.

Jack Kelly (10)
St Joseph's RC Primary School, Washington

150

Vile Victorians

The cane was hanging on a nail,
The tables were as big as a whale,
As you stood up all you could hear
was the creaking tables.

A child gets hit by a cane,
Then she cries out in pain.
The child's hand was as red
As a rose sobbing for water.

Someone made fun of my boots,
Then she took away my hoop.
It was like you could feel the
Sadness of the child crying in her heart.

Caitlin Amber McManus (10)
St Joseph's RC Primary School, Washington

A Street Scene

Dimly lit lamps flickering in the dark damp street
Well dressed adults bickering at each other
A golden mane of a brown horse is racing down the cobbled street
A rich girl's gown trails on the dirty floor.

Clip-clopping of horses' hooves on the cobbled street.
Clatter of the wooden wheels on the floor
Children laughing as they catch their hoops.

The snow drops hitting me as we are all huddling
in a group together trying to keep warm.
The gravel on my bare feet.

Brogan Edney (10)
St Joseph's RC Primary School, Washington

Bad Boring Schools

Children writing in their old mouldy copy books.
The teacher giving one of her serious looks.
Old dirty desks wobble as the children write in their books.

The whip shooting through the air.
Children screaming with pain
As they get whipped by the cane.

Strongly the teacher whips
I can just feel the pain of the
Teacher and her cane.

Sophie Crowther (10)
St Joseph's RC Primary School, Washington

The Rhyme That Brings Back Time

Chimney sweeps are sweeping
The little children are weeping
Whilst farmers are cooking some tasty meat.
That's a nice treat.
The flickering light makes children have a fright.
Clip clopping of hooves on the cobbled roads.
Children crying with pain, I've got to complain.
The splish, splashing of the water dripping into people's houses.

Olivia McMullen (10)
St Joseph's RC Primary School, Washington

War

I can feel the strong wind blowing against my face.
I can feel the ground shaking because of the bombs.
I can feel my armour getting wet.
I can see the soldiers dying in pain.
I can see the bullets being fired at our army.
I can hear soldiers shouting orders to the others.
I can hear the wind whistling in my ears.

Georgia Walmsley (10)
St Mary's RC School, Oswaldtwistle

War

Here I am in the middle of the street
Bombs being dropped everywhere around me
People fighting, people being killed
I'm so scared they might get me!
They've got my mum, they can't get me even though I've got nothing to protect me
I just want to go home and be with my mum
But all that's changed now.
I have to be stronger
I can't stand back
I have to fight up to show them I'm not dumb, not stupid
Not just a little boy
I'm the strongest soldier in this street
I'll fight them to show that I'm strong
After all I am only nine
Maybe I can punch them or kick them in the leg
Or I could even headbutt them in the head
Oohh then they'll be crying and begging me for help
They'll say that they're sorry and say they won't do it again
But I won't listen
They deserve to be locked up forever and ever and
They won't even be fed
Then I'll feed them to the tigers
That will be good
Oh no, they are coming towards me
Boom!
Argh! It's only a dream.

Isobel Moore (11)
St Mary's RC School, Oswaldtwistle

Greek Gods

I can feel the lightning in the palm of my hand.
I can see the darkness of Hades.
I can smell the fresh water of Poseidon's kingdom.
I can feel Athena's love and nature deep in my heart.
I can hear Ares' war cry.

Finbarr Fitzharris (10)
St Mary's RC School, Oswaldtwistle

Athena The Goddess

My mighty story starts here
They are all shouting in my ear.
I am on Mount Olympus
Who am I? I'm Athena

I'm the goddess of wisdom and beauty
There's a taste in my mouth
It's a tad bit fruity

I can see beautiful things
When I hear something it's the gods shouting
All I feel is my soft gold throne
My inner goddess is born

Zeus is doing my head in
It must be a sin
I ought to chuck him in the bin

My kingdom is made out of love
The metre is higher than above.

Kelsey Pilkington (10)
St Mary's RC School, Oswaldtwistle

The Horrific War!

My eyes scan the gigantic battlefield,
I watch the enemies slaughter our allies,
I gaze at bullets soaring from every metal gun.
I watch the dilapidated hospitals collapse,
I study the soldiers rushing and diving into the squelchy trenches.

My ears take in the sound of the rushing winds.
My eardrums respond as screams of pain from the injured reach my ears.
I hear the horrific booms, as the exploding bombs cascade on the blood-stained earth.
I hear the air-force soar in the bleak murky sky above.

My skin feels the drizzle of rain tumble on my drenched face.
My nerves sense the agony in my left leg.
But most of all I feel my teardrops rolling down my smudged face.

Hannah Power (10)
St Mary's RC School, Oswaldtwistle

Dinosaurs

Dinosaurs are big
Dinosaurs are fat
Some dinosaurs are small
Also some are tall
Dinosaurs are high
Some dinosaurs can fly
All the way to the sky
Dinosaurs like meat
Dinosaurs are pretty
Dinosaurs are spotty
Also some dinosaurs
Are weird dinosaurs
Are scared of enemies
Dinosaurs like leaves
From the highest trees
Dinosaurs love grass.

David Eccles (10)
St Mary's RC School, Oswaldtwistle

The Death Of Anne Boleyn

I'm so scared
It's not fair
My head is gonna be off
I just want to be in a bath
Or anywhere else for that matter
Oh Henry the nutter
I really don't want an axe on my neck
Oh heck!
I'm now in Heaven
Headless
I don't care, really
But I'm gonna haunt him
Scare him
Make him wish he was never born
Make him pay!

Anna Drury (10)
St Mary's RC School, Oswaldtwistle

155

Dinosaurs

Dinosaurs are tall.
Dinosaurs are small.
Dinosaurs can fly right up to the sky.
Dinosaurs bite, mostly they put up a fight.
Dinosaurs are bad.
Dinosaurs are mostly not sad.
Dinosaurs are heard before.
Dinosaurs are carnivores.
Dinosaurs are large and small.
Diplodocus biggest of all.

Callum Dunn (10)
St Mary's RC School, Oswaldtwistle

Roman Entertainment

I can hear lions roaring
Millions of people cheering
Gladiators clanking in their armour
People gasping really loud
I can see blood everywhere around me
Bulls charging into people
Gladiators battling each other for entertainment to Roman civilisations
I can feel my heart beating fast
My brain springing around like a rocket
My legs shaking like crazy.

Marley Cooper (10)
St Mary's RC School, Oswaldtwistle

Greek Gods

G ods
R oaring voices
E lated that the war is over
E lectric power from the lightning bolt
K ronos, king of time
S ea is ruled by Poseidon.

Niamh Kay (10)
St Mary's RC School, Oswaldtwistle

Henry The Eighth

Divorced, beheaded, died, divorced, beheaded, survived.
I am Henry the Eighth
I had six sorry wives
You could say I ruined their lives!
Anne Boleyn she was one
She failed to give me a son
So the axe sent poor Anne to her grave
Urrgh!
But now I have to go . . .
Because I'm sending someone to their grave – cut!

Isabel Macauley (10)
St Mary's RC School, Oswaldtwistle

Henry – Born To Get Married

Yesterday I got married to Anne, she died
Today I got married to Catherine, one minute
See you later Catherine,
Tomorrow I'm going to get married to Jane,
that's not going to go well.
In the future I'm going to get married again,
Oh look, there's a lady named Catherine too
'Let's get married!' I asked,
Okay I guess I need to get married again then.

Abigail Rawnsley (10)
St Mary's RC School, Oswaldtwistle

Dinosaurs

I can see the dinosaur egg hatch
I can hear the dinosaur roar
I can feel the dinosaur's breath on my neck
I can hear the dinosaurs stomp
I can feel the ground shake
I can see all the dinosaurs around me
I can see lots of footprints.

Leona Howarth (11)
St Mary's RC School, Oswaldtwistle

157

Dinosaurs

There was a dinosaur
Who liked to snore
He wasn't a bore
That dinosaur.

He had a big roar
His teeth were white and sharp
His scaly skin green.

That dinosaur, I think he might be mean.

Marianna Morante (10)
St Mary's RC School, Oswaldtwistle

War

I can hear the shots of guns
Also the bang of bombs.
I can see the houses on fire.
I can smell the burn of fire.
I can taste the smoke in my mouth.
I can feel upset that people are dying.
Also angry that sick people around the world make people suffer.

Aspen Feathers (11)
St Mary's RC School, Oswaldtwistle

King Henry

When I travelled back in time
I saw five headless ghosts
I heard a big thumping noise
It was King Henry VIII
There was blood all over
I fainted.

Kyra Beetham (10)
St Mary's RC School, Oswaldtwistle

War!

I can hear the bombs crackling the sky.
I can see the people dying in pain.
I can hear the machines rolling along the roads.
I can taste the smoke from the bombs.
I can hear the guns shooting.
I can hear the people crying because family are dying.

Skye Perosa-Brierley (10)
St Mary's RC School, Oswaldtwistle

There Was An Old Dinosaur

There was an old dinosaur called Eric
He liked to be hysteric
He wasn't a bore
He liked to roar
That little dinosaur called Eric.

Ellie Chamberlain (10)
St Mary's RC School, Oswaldtwistle

Henry VIII

Henry the eighth was a very fat king
His friends said he could not sing
So he married Catherine
Who could sing so she wrote a hymn
Henry did not like the hymn so that was the end of Catherine
His next best friend was Anne Boleyn
Who could not sing
So that was also the end of Anne Boleyn
After the lives of another three wives
Henry remembered that ancient hymn
Which reminded him of the first Catherine
Then he noticed Katherine Parr who he admired from afar
Then they got married in a bar
And lived happily ever after.

Henry Ashton (9)
St Peter's Elwick Primary School, Elwiok

159

Henry VIII

H enry was a king in the sixteenth century
E leven children he had but only three survived, the rest were buried in the cemetery
N atural causes was the reason for their deaths, he wanted a son so this is why he tried for so many
R eformation, the break with Rome and the Pope would not let him break up his first home
Y oung prince Henry became king in 1509, he married his dead brother's wife Catherine of Aaragon

T hey had many kids together but only one survived, Mary who became the queen
H is wives all had similar names: Catherines, Annes and Jane. One died, two executed, two divorced, one widowed.
E lizabeth and Edward were the other two children who also became monarchs of England

E ating was one of Henry's favourite habits along with music and sports
I talian was one of the many languages he spoke.
G reenwich is where he was born and where he died.
H enry ruled by hatred and fear and when he died no one shed a tear.
T ennis was a sport young Henry enjoyed to play but later in life he became as big as a whale
H enry was 38 when he was laid to rest, his wife did not care. A few months later she married Thomas Seymour and he was her best.

Charlie Elsdon (9)
St Peter's Elwick Primary School, Elwick

Elizabeth I

Elizabeth, Elizabeth, Elizabeth the 1st,
When she died everybody cursed.
Such a good queen and such a good heart,
That's what set Elizabeth apart.
Everybody liked her, everybody loved,
That's why Elizabeth never got shoved.
Off the throne and into her grave,
Because she was strong and she was brave.

Emma Londesbrough (9)
St Peter's Elwick Primary School, Elwick

Henry VIII

Henry VIII was a very big guy.
He had six wives, all but three die.
Catherine of Aragon, her he divorced.
Anne Boleyn was next of course.
Unfortunately her head did roll
She was not a lucky soul.
Jane Seymour was the next to die.
Then to Anne of Cleves he said goodbye.
Catherine Howard, her head was chopped.
But Katherine Parr survived the lot.
Henry had started life quite fit
He loved to play tennis and wrestled a bit.
The problem was he loved his food.
So he got quite fat (sorry to be rude).
The people who served King Henry VIII
Did not like how their money was spent.
He taxed them loads
To pay for war
And still he always wanted more.
In 1547 he lay down and died
His name was King Henry VIII.

Joel McKimmie (10)
St Peter's Elwick Primary School, Elwick

Henry VIII

Henry VIII, six wives he had
Some folk say he was horrid and mad
Twice he ordered, 'Off with her head!'
The guards always did whatever he said
Two were divorced, he spared their lives
They were the two very fortunate wives
His third wife Jane very sadly died
This is the only wife for whom Henry cried
Lucky Katherine outlived the king
So people on the street began to sing.

Louis Harll (10)
St Peter's Elwick Primary School, Elwick

141

Henry VIII

This king is remembered for his six wives
More than many men would have in six lives.
He did so much more in his fifty-five years
But he ate so much he couldn't walk up the stairs.

He was a musician, an author and a poet
But if he really loved his wives he didn't seem to show it.
Poor Catherine of Aragon was his first
But she did not suffer the worst.

Two were divorced and one poor soul died
Two lost their heads and the other survived.
He was a great king as everyone knows
But my gosh I wouldn't like to have been one of his foes.

Holly Lister (10)
St Peter's Elwick Primary School, Elwick

The Tudor Ship

100 sailors were onboard,
Some people worked whilst others snored.
Most people were asleep,
Others steered the ship into the deep.
The next day they found some land,
It was full of rocks and a lot of sand.
One sailor went to check on the crow's nest,
There was a rat up there which was a pest.
In the evening, a sailor scrubbed the floor,
Ready for tomorrow when they would set out and explore.

Kate Cowan (10)
St Peter's Elwick Primary School, Elwick

Henry The Horrible

H orrible
E xcellent
N aughty
R ough
Y oung

V ictorious
I ntelligent
L arge
E ducated.

Kaytlin Hennells-Barber (10)
St Peter's Elwick Primary School, Elwick

Henry VIII

In Tudor times there was a prince and Henry was his name
At eighteen years old the prince became bold and started his rule as king
He was considered well-educated, spoke four languages and wrote poetry
A handsome young king who loved to sing.
He composed 'Helas Madame;
Unfortunately after a while many thought of him as vile
The overweight boss you didn't want to cross or it would be off with your head!
Six wives with two gone! And one sickly son
Died 18th January 1547.

Oliver Stone (10)
St Peter's Elwick Primary School, Elwick

Henry Tudor

The two roses, red and white,
Gave some people quite a fright.
Their three young daughters Margaret, Elizabeth and Mary,
Who knows if they ever dreamed of being a fairy?
They also had three handsome sons you know, Arthur, Edmund and Henry,
The last mentioned didn't come across so friendly.
I will now start a game of poker,
With Henry Tudor's favourite joker.

Kaylyn Keenan (10)
St Peter's Elwick Primary School, Elwick

Henry VIII

Can we make a rhyme on the Tudor times?
Especially on a king called Henry,
He was a king at 17,
He was renowned for being mean,
Because he had six wives,
But took their lives.

Chloe Dring (9)
St Peter's Elwick Primary School, Elwick

Henry VIII

Henry, Henry seemed so friendly
However that all changed
When his six wives came
Henry, Henry seemed so sad
For the son he never had.

Suzanne Bird (10)
St Peter's Elwick Primary School, Elwick

Henry

H e had six wives and three children also he had health problems
E njoyed his food, especially meat
N ot a vegetarian
R uled and reigned over England
Y ou would not want to come across him.

Lucy Brown (10)
St Peter's Elwick Primary School, Elwick

Henry VIII

Henry the 8th was big.
His favourite animal was a pig.
He tried to fly.
Landed dry.
He bought a pig called Fig.

Jessica Corrigan (9)
St Peter's Elwick Primary School, Elwick

Ancient Poems

Romans

They feared Romans with swords and shields,
They would usually go battle on the high fields,
The parents teaching their kids to battle,
And then they'd go fight with their horse and saddle.

Egyptians

The poor tired Egyptians work all day,
But no matter how hard they work they get no pay,
And all the poor Egyptians are defenceless slaves,
So that the rich Egyptians don't live in caves.

Cavemen

Cavemen eat mammoth all through the day,
Then they make block sculptures out of clay,
Then get ready for hunting with their pointy spears,
And then they go hunting for mammoth and deer.

Tudors

All the Tudors like to smash and beat,
But most of them prefer to eat meat,
The Tudors use their windows to poo and pee,
And someone once pooed and it landed on me!

Timea Dunnery (11)
Stanhope Barrington Primary School, Stanhope

Fun Fun History

One soldier was playing with his gun
Then he stopped to eat a bun
One soldier was flying a twin engine p-38 lighting jet
Then he stopped to play with his pet

King Henry
Was unfriendly
He chopped off two wives heads
They turned up dead

Long walk the ants
All round the plants
The dinosaur did snore
Suddenly it started to roar

One Roman pulled out his sword
Then he had to visit the medical ward
He used his lucky shield
Out on the battlefield

There were some yucky cures
People wandered around the city sewers
Queen Victoria was thrown
Up onto the throne

One Indian fired a bow
The arrow stubbed another Indian's toe
One Indian was up on his horse
They ran an international course

They wore kilts to battle
They also herded up cattle
They used a sword and shield
Out on the battlefield.

Louise Unsworth (10)
Stanhope Barrington Primary School, Stanhope

The Deathly World War II

The sky is filled with invisible bombs, flashing bright lights before me.
I can see the deathly flames rising above trees, buildings.

Soaring planes trying to kill the enemy
Bombs flying all over blood is everywhere I look.
Brave men fighting people screaming
Where have they gone?

I can smell the ashes and the corpses laying on the ground
I can smell the fire
'Argh!' a dead body has just fallen in front of me
Blood all over
When will the war end?

I can feel the fear of all the people,
Crying, squealing and swarming all over.
I can feel the blood on my shoes, and bombs blowing up buildings and houses.
I think I might cry my hair is dyeing black because of all the ashes.

The World War II has come to an end, glad it is over.

Lauren Lee (10)
Stanhope Barrington Primary School, Stanhope

Romans And Tudors

The Romans marching with their shields,
All walking on a muddy field.
They've got on their armour,
But he isn't happy, the farmer,
They are ready to fight with their swords,
But they are feeling a bit bored.

Next to the Tudors,
They were the rulers.
King Henry was unfriendly,
He had six wives who are dead.
He chopped off one's head,
Her blood was bright red, and what did he do to the rest?
Divorces, beheaded and died,
Divorced, beheaded, survived!

Emily Vasey (10)
Stanhope Barrington Primary School, Stanhope

147

Rhyming History

Dinosaur's dash!
In the giant jungle opening dinosaurs roar
In the giant jungle opening dinosaurs snore
In the giant jungle opening dinosaurs got bored
In the giant jungle opening dinosaurs tore.

Caveman!
Caveman, caveman, caveman, *smash!*
Caveman, caveman, caveman, *bash!*
Caveman, caveman, caveman, *crash!*
Caveman, caveman, caveman, *mash!*
Caveman, caveman, caveman, *thrash!*

Roman Thrashes!
Romans, Romans defended the wall!
Romans, Romans fix the wall!
Romans, Romans defend the wall!
Romans, Romans demolished the wall!

George Haynes (10)
Stanhope Barrington Primary School, Stanhope

The Blitz

Day after day
Bombs drop down
Destroying buildings
On the ground

People scurrying
Like ants all around
Sirens calling out
That loud

Blitz is bad
But it was had
WWII is now through
Who would do this?
I know it was you – *Hitler.*

Aaron Palmer (10)
Stockton Wood CP School, Speke

World War II Poem

Bombs exploding here and there,
Bullets flying in the air,
People screaming everywhere,
Running for their life,
Looking for shelter,
Children evacuated on the train,
Parents crying in the rain,
Children awake all night,
Thinking if their parents are alright.

Erin Catterall (10)
Stockton Wood CP School, Speke

The Terrific Titanic

You can feel the boat bobbing up and down on top of the water and the wind
rushing past you.
People feel really scared because there is a great big iceberg coming towards
them.

You can feel the wind on the back of your neck,
but if it is sunny you can feel the sun on your back.

You can see another boat slowly coming towards you.
You can see dark shadows of sea creatures in the water.
A great big cold iceberg coming towards the boat!

Emily Thorpe (8)
Stoneraise Primary School, Stoneraise

A Roman Soldier

I see ferocious enemies marching towards me.
Their armour looks heavy and hard.
I hear swords clanking together as we fight.
The sound of blood-curdling screams fills the air.
I feel my tummy rumbling like a growling monster.
I feel sad because the battle goes on forever and ever.

Tom Beverley, Robin McCallum, Jessica Bell,
Cameron Davies & Lewis Wardrope (7)
Stoneraise Primary School, Stoneraise

149

Viking Poem

Vikings hated begin cremated
One saw a fish and nearly fainted.
He hit the fish on the head.
Then the fish was super dead.
Vikings hated to swim in moats.
Vikings didn't like wearing coats.
Hunting food, the hungry Viking,
Up the mountain he went hiking.

Ruaridh MacLeod (8)
Torridon Primary School, Torridon

A Viking Raid

All I can see are choppy waves and sweaty men pulling and pushing on the oars
in front of me,
Sparkling treasure glistening and glinting in the sun,
Struggling slaves screaming, yelling and begging for mercy,
A monk's monastery burning in the sun.

The seagulls going, 'Cheep, cheep, cheep,'
I don't think I'm going to sleep.
Waves crashing on the boat, it's rocking fiercely now,
The men panting on the oars,
The animals making lots of noise.

Cold, wooden, heavy oars and my bloody metal sword,
A heavy helmet on my head,
Sweat pouring down my face,
I'm sad and excited, it's really quite weird.

Stale cheese and bread,
Wine and water, it's really quite dirty too,
Tastes so much of stale, stale goo,
Seeds and meat going down my throat, I think I'm going to be sick on the boat.

I hope to get all our treasure,
And get back to my family in Scandinavia,
I dream of getting some slaves for me,
I hope I don't fall in the cold, cold sea.

Esme Johnson (8)
Uplawmoor Primary School, Uplawmoor

A Viking Raid

A fierce looking figure head and huge blue waves.
The huge red and white sail blowing in the wind.
Petrified people pushing and pulling on the oars
And the sun setting behind the green hills.
The burning monasteries in the horizon.

The heavy wind moaning and whistling and oars hitting off the water.
The dark blue water whooshing in the cold wind.
Men whining as they move the oars.
Monks screaming in the burning monasteries.

The damp wooden floor and the tall brown mast.
Excited and scared in case we get lost and in case we find something.
Leather armour and hard metal helmet.
The wooden oars in my hands.

Salt from the water and old brown bread.
Horrid meat and rotten fruit and freezing water.
Disgusting wine from the defeated enemies.
Sweat dripping into my mouth from rowing.

Lots of silver and even more gold.
A new home with more sunshine and less rain and snow.
All sorts of valuable items including rubies and sapphires.
To burn 100 monasteries or more.

Liam Catterson (8)
Uplawmoor Primary School, Uplawmoor

A Viking Raid

Choppy waves crashing against the boat
Seagulls flying overhead
Petrified people pushing and pulling on the oars
The fierce figurehead on the boat

The wind whistling in the sky
Vikings groaning as they row
Seagulls singing over the blue sea
The boat going over bumpy waves

The cold heavy oars
The wind blowing in my face
My tummy rumbling as I row
I also feel excited

Sea salt from the sea
Seed and meat from lunch time
The watery wine we stole from the monastery
The stinky smell of people going past

Hopefully I will return back to my family
And won't die before we get there
I hope we win the raid and get some gold
I hope the Vikings don't leave without me.

Bobbi McIsaac (9)
Uplawmoor Primary School, Uplawmoor

A Viking Raid

Choppy waves crashing into the side of the boat,
Petrified Vikings pushing and pulling on the oars,
Seagulls flying over the top of the ship,
A scary figure head on the front of the boat.

Fast fish jumping in and out of the water,
Fierce Vikings eating and drinking meat and wine,
Seagulls singing at the side of the ship,
The oars hitting the top of the water.

The wind shouting past the side of the boat,
The slippery wood of the heavy oars,
The heavy oars going up and down,
The boat moving over the bumpy waves.

The salty horrible taste of the choppy waves,
The blank taste of the monk's blood,
The meat and wine they stole from the monks,
The salty taste of the fat fish.

Staying alive and going again,
We win the raid and get lots of gold,
We win the land and rule it forever,
Some getting lost at sea and never returning.

Luca Ventisei (9)
Uplawmoor Primary School, Uplawmoor

A Viking Raid

The sun setting behind small scared sheep,
The ghastly figurehead staring down at me,
The vicious Viking leader looking fierce,
He is standing behind the symmetrical sail.

The seagulls are screeching above me,
Wailing slaves are not helping,
The creaking of the planks from the swaying mast,
Whilst the pitter patter of the rain follows.

I'm feeling more determined, most contented in my job,
The rampaging rain is pouring, pouring over me,
I'm feeling so much sweat right now and
Spiky wood from the oars.

Seasalt is spraying in my mouth and a mixture of sand follows,
Cold meat and porridge for meals,
Blood coming out of my hands,
I also taste sweat coming off my face.

I hope for a pit full of treasure,
Maybe even books we adore,
When we get back there will be loads of respect,
New lands and so much more.

Eve Elisabeth Wengel (9)
Uplawmoor Primary School, Uplawmoor

A Viking Raid

Petrified people pushing and pulling,
Choppy waves all over the place,
Swimming fish whooshing in the ocean,
And a fierce looking figurehead.

The wind whistling all over the place,
The water rippling,
Trees swaying in the breeze,
And Vikings panting.

I feel terribly tired,
I have been rowing for ages,
I also feel excited and exhilarated,
I'm exhausted and angry.

I taste splashes of salt water,
Dry beef,
Normal water,
And sometimes wine.

I dream of getting lots of gold,
And treasure
Maybe some money
And more swords and shields.

Stephanie Frutin (8)
Uplawmoor Primary School, Uplawmoor

A Viking Raid

Choppy waves crashing against the boat,
Fast fish swimming furiously through the water, staying afloat.
Petrified people pushing and pulling on the oars,
Sheep on the hills where the sun's setting.

The Vikings grunting, pulling on the oars,
The waves crashing into each other,
The wind wildly whistling in all directions,
The slaves groaning in the background.

The boat rocking by the waves,
The wind blowing in my face,
The wood on the oars, I'm pushing in a good pace,
I also feel very excited and sad.

The salty air from the sea,
Stale cheese which has been there for a long time,
The wine that we brought with us which is so divine,
The seeds and the meat cooking.

Winning the massive raid,
Getting the land we wanted,
Hopefully not getting lost out at sea,
Staying alive and seeing my family who will be happy to see me.

Katie Raeside (8)
Uplawmoor Primary School, Uplawmoor

A Viking Raid

Petrified people heaving on the heavy oars
The sun setting on the burning monastery
Clear skies for good luck
Soaring seagulls swishing overhead

The sails bashing on the barky wood
Water splashing relentlessly on the side of the boat
People screaming in the burning monasteries
The wind blowing in my ear

The sea splashing in my hands
The rough wood on the cold oars
I feel outraged and excited
The searing sores from the rough oars

Wine we stole from the opposing team
The salt water splashing in my mouth while I motor on the oars
The stale, rough bread made from barley we brought from Norway
Rough revenge after the English

Cheering children in the streets
Wealth and health for my family
Still warm water sailing down the rivers
Big brown books stacked up in my house.

Morgan Whiteford (9)
Uplawmoor Primary School, Uplawmoor

A Viking Raid

Sun gleaming down on the ship deck,
Vicious Vikings rowing as hard as they can,
Petrified slaves getting chucked over both sides of the giant ship.
Massive waves coming towards the ship.

Howling strong winds in my ear,
Dark, murky water splashing against the hard wooden oars,
Flaming fiery monasteries burning in the distance,
Cries of monks running away.

Waves clashing against the vicious looking figurehead,
I feel the heat of the boiling sunset in the far distance,
I feel excited about the journey to come,
I'm worried about my family.

Salty taste of sweat dripping from my face
Stone cold meat inside my mouth,
Apples for snacks,
Water splashing in my face while I row.

I hope to find new lands,
And to be a famous Viking,
To have books and riches,
More supplies for journeys to come.

Josh Fraser (9)
Uplawmoor Primary School, Uplawmoor

A Viking Raid

Wooden oars splashing and crashing, ripping and rumbling,
Sailing us through the dark and choppy seas.
Monks shouting, screaming, praying and being thrown overboard.
Treasures, food wine and weapons.
The dark, choppy and electrifying horizons.

Monks praying, monks shouting, monks screaming, monks bellowing at us in another language.
Choppy seas throwing the boat up and down *boom*.
I hear other Vikings yelping with pain.
Jugs of wine clinking and clanging, crashing and bashing.

Overwhelmed by our power to outwit the enemy.
Happy for ourselves to bring so many things home.
I also feel a bit sorry for the slaves but not much.
Wooden oars giving me splinters all the time.

Salty water splashing up from the sea.
Horrid wine from our families.
Fruit from the old monasteries.
Some nice cold raw meat.

Jason Robb (9)
Uplawmoor Primary School, Uplawmoor

A Viking Raid

Choppy waves turning the sail inside out
Slaves rowing so hard that their arms can't bear it anymore
The map to show us where we are going
Rocks smashing off the boat.

The wind whistling wildly
Slaves moaning because they are bored
Captain shouting, 'Aye aye! Land ahoy!'
Jingling treasures.

My heart pumping
Jaggy bits on my armour
My hands getting wetter because of slaves being nervous
Sharks in the water eating the slaves that have been thrown in.

Erin Cupples (8)
Uplawmoor Primary School, Uplawmoor

A Viking Raid

Men huffing and puffing, pushing and pulling.
The waves are roaring and splashing.
Tons of gold and silver treasure.
Enemy boats docking into their village.

The splashing of the waves against the boat.
The captain giving orders.
The wind whistling past.
The sound of men huffing and puffing.

Brave and fearless, my heavy helmet, sword and shield.
A light breeze and the wood of the oar.
Excited and full of joy, waiting to attack the village.
The wind blowing in my face.

Reuben Gallagher (8)
Uplawmoor Primary School, Uplawmoor

A Viking Raid

Choppy waves hitting the boat,
Scary dragon head on the top.
Sun on the horizon.
Sheep eating the grass on the hills.

Wet wood on the oars.
Strong ship on the sea.
Heavy armour on my body.
Monks' blood on the boat.

Birds whistling in the sky.
Trees rising on the hills.
Waves crashing on the boat.
Wind blowing on the sea.

Declan Kee (8)
Uplawmoor Primary School, Uplawmoor

A Viking Raid

Scary figure head on the top of the boat.
The sea crashing on the rocks.
The rain falling on the boat.
Fish swimming in the sea and the rain on my hand.

Seagulls singing in the sky.
The wind whistling in the sky.
Waves waving in the wind.
Scared servants on the boat.

The wind waving in my hair.
The wood on the boat.
Myself shivering on the boat.
The rain tapping on my head.

Lauren Rose Sanders (6)
Uplawmoor Primary School, Uplawmoor

A Viking Raid

Sun setting over the Viking village and the people.
Men rowing hard on the oars while a storm comes.
The dragon head on the top of the ship is scary.
Seagulls fly over the ship while the ship moves.

The waves pushing against the boat.
The cold, wet wooden oars.
Excited.
Sad as I'm leaving my family.

Waves splashing at the back of the boat.
I hear the people screaming,
Houses burning.
The monastery bell ringing.

Innes Carslaw (8)
Uplawmoor Primary School, Uplawmoor

A Viking Raid

Strange shapes in the sky,
Seagulls soaring way up high,
Sleeping sheep on the hills,
Smelly and sweaty people pushing and pulling,

Worried people whispering to each other,
Wonderful waves splashing against the boat,
Seagulls singing in the sky,
The captain crying this way and that way.

Wild wind whooshing through my hair,
Everyone is extremely excited to find the new land,
Sweat running down my back,
Cold people shivering because there is a storm.

Niamh Presslie (7)
Uplawmoor Primary School, Uplawmoor

A Viking Raid

The dark shadow of the boat reflecting on the water.
Fierce looking figurehead leading on front.
Slaves getting thrown overboard.
Sparkling treasure stolen from the village.

Worried people whispering to each other.
The seagulls singing in the dark sky.
The loud lightning and thunder in the sky.
The choppy waves splashing on the boat.

The gasping wind blowing the sail very hard.
The salt water hitting our skin.
Sweat running down my back.
People shivering because there is a cold, wet storm.

Amy Cupples (7)
Uplawmoor Primary School, Uplawmoor

A Viking Raid

The wild waves
Strong men pushing and pulling
Big wooden boats
Poor people falling off the fast boats

The captain singing in the toilet
Wind blowing round in circles
The water splashing against the boat
I can hear the people talking

I can feel the big men touching me on the arm
I can feel the air blowing
I feel the rocks touching the boats
I feel myself shaking.

Katie Kerrigan (7)
Uplawmoor Primary School, Uplawmoor

A Viking Raid

Fierce looking figurehead.
Fish.
Sparkling treasure.
Waves splashing.

Wind whistling.
People screaming,
Burning monastery.
Arrows flying.

Wind in your hair.
Treasure.
Helmets.
Oars in your hand.

Dean Grierson (7)
Uplawmoor Primary School, Uplawmoor

163

The RAF vs Jagdwaffe

I see a two metre bomb
Their guns shoot my friend
The Jagdwaffe in my sights
I see the flames of a raging fire

I feel blood from my legs
A depressing feeling
The controls fill with blood
I feel strong

I hear Jagdwaffe bombs
My friend David's guns
I hear no engine
I hear nothing
Oh well . . .

Dylan Leask (11)
Urafirth Primary School, Shetland Islands

WWII

I see German aircrafts behind me all green and grey
I see smoke pouring from the side of my Spitfire all cloudy
Germans trying to bomb London
Dark bombs all over the place

I feel sad cos I got picked to go and fight in the air
Upset in case I might die
I feel excitement to see all the German aircrafts
I feel disappointed cos I want to go to Germany

I hear the sirens of London telling the people to get in the
bomb shelters
The whistles of bombs beside me
The mission control on the radio
Enemy planes creeping behind my Spitfire.

Jenna Maree Mowat (10)
Urafirth Primary School, Shetland Islands

Bomber's Story

I see bombs being dropped.
I see smoke coming from my friend's plane.
I see places getting bombed.
I see bombs exploding on the ground.

I feel devastated because my family is in great danger.
I am homesick because I miss my family.
I feel worried that I might not make it.
I am scared because a plane might smash into me.

I hear guns shooting at my enemy.
I hear whistling noises from the bombs.
I hear the engine making guzzling noises.
I hear big explosions coming from below me.

Cassie Gilbertson (9)
Urafirth Primary School, Shetland Islands

WWII

I see the land below me, it's green
I see the sea in the distance shimmering dark
The enemy aircraft shooting at us
The enemy aircraft bombing buildings

I am scared I might crash
Depressed my training was so short
My first time at flying
I'm going to die!

Guns shooting at me
Bombs exploding
Enemy aircraft gunfire
Shower of bombs falling to Manchester.

Rhys Missenden (11)
Urafirth Primary School, Shetland Islands

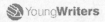

WWII Pilot

I can see the orange flame go up and black smoke
I can see the yellow light of the guns
I can see the black smoke
I can see bombed air fields go up in flames.

I feel scared in case I die
I feel scared for my friends
I might not see them again
I feel worried that I won't make it

I can hear the roar of the engine
I can hear the plane roaring past me
I can hear the bombs going off in a bang I can hear the gunfire whistle past me.

David Poleson (10)
Urafirth Primary School, Shetland Islands

Scribbler! Magazine

If you enjoy reading and writing you will love Scribbler! Magazine.
Scribbler! Magazine will teach you new skills and build confidence
in your writing, whilst giving you lots of fun and entertainment.

We receive 100% positive feedback and are proud to say that
Scribbler! is the leading reading and writing magazine for 7-11
year olds. Jam packed with workshops, competitions, reviews and
lots more, Scribbler! will keep you entertained for hours.
To find out more about Scribbler! Magazine please visit our
website **www.scribblermagazine.com**

Young Writers Information

We hope you have enjoyed reading
this book - and that you will continue
to enjoy it in the coming years.

If you like reading and writing
poetry drop us a line, or give
us a call, and we'll send you
a free information pack.

Alternatively if you would like to order further
copies of this book or any of our other titles,
then please give us a call or log onto our
website at www.youngwriters.co.uk

Young Writers Information
Remus House
Coltsfoot Drive
Peterborough
PE2 9BF
(01733) 890066